FIG JAM AND FOXTROT

Tales of life, love and food in the Karoo

FIG JAM
AND FOXTROT

Tales of life, love and food in the Karoo

LYNN BEDFORD HALL
illustrated by TONY GROGAN

Author's acknowledgements

I started with an idea. Slowly translated it into words. About a trillion words. The trillion words turned into stories, which went into my computer to be mulled over, crossed out, rewritten, plots reinvented – oh, it took months of slog and times of despair and then moments of such satisfaction I was heady with bubbles, like a bottle of champagne. Stories done, I had to head for the kitchen for a long, long time, perhaps a million days or so. In the end I had a book. But no – you can't have a book without a team: a publishing manager to give you the green light, offer a contract, appoint an editor, a designer, an illustrator, a proofreader … It's all a case of team work, and in *Fig Jam and Foxtrot* I have had the finest bunch on earth. Linda, bless her, first saw the possibilities and gave me Joy as an editor. Now this woman is a total treasure, and every author should have the privilege of a smiling, incredibly competent Joy Clack on tap. She'll treat your manuscript as though it were a rare diamond. Work long, long hours at shaping it. Quickly detect any flaws. Smooth out the cuts, then give a professional polish. Sean Robertson and Petal Palmer's enthusiasm for Tony's sketches matched my own. We yelped with delight at his brilliant interpretations of the characters and Sean harnessed his own considerable creative talent in painstakingly hand-lettering all the titles, and worked overtime to fit the illustrations in just the right places. My family wasn't part of the team but my thanks certainly extend to them, for they quietly evaluated my work (both literary and gustatory) and – they're very honest, they are – gave me the thumbs up wherever they felt it was due. Now I have finished.
Thanks again, everyone.
Lynn Bedford Hall

First published in 2003 by
Struik Publishers (a division of New Holland
   Publishing (South Africa) (Pty) Ltd)
Cornelis Struik House
80 McKenzie Street
Cape Town 8001
www.struik.co.za

New Holland Publishing is a member of the
Johnnic Publishing Group

Copyright © in published edition: Struik
   Publishers 2003
Copyright © in text: Lynn Bedford Hall 2003
Copyright © in illustrations: Tony Grogan/
   Struik Image Library 2003

Log on to our photographic website
www.imagesofafrica.co.za for an
African experience

10 9 8 7 6 5 4 3 2

Publishing Manager: Linda de Villiers
Editor: Joy Clack
Designer: Sean Robertson
Illustrator: Tony Grogan

Reproduction by Hirt & Carter Cape (Pty) Ltd
Printed and bound by Kyodo Printing Co
   (Singapore) Pte Ltd

ISBN 1 86872 868 4

CONTENTS

Author's Introduction

Once upon a time I used to climb the oak tree in our garden and talk to the creatures that lived in the knot-holes in the branches. I knew they were there, I just had to whisper softly for them to hear me. They were my friends and through them I discovered the magical world of make-believe. I couldn't set down these conversations because I couldn't write at that age, but this internal world has never left me. We all have a desire to create and as I grew older my need found expression in two spheres: writing and cooking. I think I was eleven when I had my first poem published. It went something like this:

*'My classroom is in such a lovely school
Where trees are shady and leafy and cool.'*

I'll spare you the rest. At about the same time I started messing around in the kitchen. My best invention was a milkshake made with condensed milk and ginger ale. Now all this sounds quite horrifying, but everything improved as I grew up, and this is where these stories come into play.

The small Karoo town about which I write exists, but I have altered the name because that allows me more licence. Like all towns, it has changed over the years, but at that time it was simply the happiest place for a child to be, offering glorious freedom in a sheltered world of gentle people. As I remember it, the days were hot and still but for the soft strumming of cicadas; the sunsets were unfailingly brilliant and the night sky as bright as an eternal Christmas tree. I also remember the women: in my child's mind they were always plump and powdered and smelling of eau-de-cologne. They sat me on their laps and gave me slivers of biltong.

Aspects of my home life that probably helped to shape me were my parents' love of books, music and good food. They were a prominent couple in the community. We knew all the inhabitants of the town and district, and I was taught to respect everyone and never, ever to repeat any secrets or gossip. I must, therefore, have become a voyeur at an early age and locked a thousand secrets in my head, for there were scandals aplenty – adulterous affairs and deliciously wicked goings-on – all to be tucked in deep and not spoken about.

And yet, despite the odd bit of scandal, it was a town and district in which lived truly kind and noble people, and the true essence of the place is still as real to me as it ever was. THE STORIES I HAVE WRITTEN ARE, IN A WAY, A TRIBUTE TO THOSE I REMEMBER AND LOVED.

Food plays a big part in small towns. Whether it's a bazaar or a sports meeting, a wedding or a funeral, people eat when they meet. And with no take-aways, home cooking was very important. Women became quite famous for their personal specialities, and you never went visiting without a little gift in a basket. My mother (who loved good food) did not enjoy cooking – we had an excellent cook who took care of that side of things. But her sister, my aunt, who lived on a large farm outside the town, was an adventurous cook with the most wonderful ingredients at hand. So this was the perfect combination – at home I was allowed to occupy the kitchen as much as I liked, and on the farm I could learn from my dear, patient aunt.

Now put all these factors together and perhaps the reason for this book will become clear. In these women of Corriebush, I have been able to interpret my life in a country town, indulge my compulsion to write, and incorporate my career as an author and food and travel journalist. Although the women are fictitious, I have attributed the recipes to them, firstly imagining what they might have cooked and then updating the recipes to suit today's tastes. They have been devised, tried and tested by me, and the result is a book in which fact and fiction are combined to create a cookbook with a difference. I hope it will be an enjoyable read, with some useful recipes, but as Sophia would say, 'Remember, *liefie,* the proof is in the trifle.'

'*Pudding*, Sophia.'

'I *said* pudding.'

Who is Sophia? To find out, read on.

INTRODUCTION

I was born in Corriebush, not far from the railway station. In those days nothing was far from the railway station, because Corriebush was a small town and the station was right there in the middle of it. In fact, it still is, because unlike some Karoo towns, Corriebush never grew big. To this day the town murmurs there quietly, a softly beating heart in the middle of the wrinkled veld. But the trains don't run there anymore. The platform is still there, and so is the railway line. I remember how the trains would shunt off slowly and then, gathering speed, embrace the town in a wide, proud loop before escaping across the veld to the north. But the trains don't run anymore because the council, having observed the dwindling numbers of passengers and half-empty trucks, decided it was a waste of money laying on trains to Corriebush.

And so the town never grew, and today it is almost as it was when I was a child. The same white-washed houses with wide stoeps and gables, flower gardens in the front, vegetables at the back. The same church with a clock and a soaring white steeple. The Corner Shop is still there, and the shopkeepers still lock up over the lunch-hour in summer, so that they can go home to rest behind shutters closed against the midday heat.

A humped mountain cradles Corriebush, and so the rising sun never bursts onto the town. The rays spill gently down the flanks of the berg, and that is why every day dawns slowly and quietly, soft as a Sunday. By late afternoon the sweltering sun has burnt itself out, and it simply falls abruptly into a hole at the edge of the veld. That is what I believed, anyway, and I imagined that it lay there panting until darkness came and smothered its flames, and the night dropped down in a hush of yellow stars. Sometimes, tucked up in my bed, I would hear a baboon barking in a distant mountain kloof. But I was safe and snug and I knew that, next day, the sun would once again flow down the mountain and into my town. This was a wonderful place in which to grow up and my childhood was innocent and happy.

The stories I hold come from Aunt Lovey.

Aunt Lovey lived in the house next door. Her real name was Miss Lavelle Douw, but nobody called her that. It was always Aunt Lovey, or Tannie or Aunty but never Lavelle, and only the *dominee* called her Miss Douw. In a way, Aunt Lovey could be called the founder of Corriebush, for she was there from the time the first people bought plots and built houses.

Originally, the whole area had belonged to her father, Kerneels Douw, who had inherited the family farm from *his* father round about the end of the nineteenth century. But a cruel drought lasting five years had forced Kerneels to sell off portions of his land to avoid going bankrupt. In time, these little plots joined up and Corriebush was born – a cluster of houses spread around the old Douw homestead. No longer able to farm sheep, Kerneels sold off his stock and turned to small-scale vegetable farming, and so the family was able to stay on their land.

When her parents died within a month of each other, Aunt Lovey locked their bedroom door and never opened it again. She stayed on in the old home, growing vegetables and breeding fine Austrolorp fowls, and when she wasn't busy with either her garden or her hens, she would sit on the front stoep or, in bad weather, in the *voorkamer*, and watch what she called the goings-on in the town. She knew all the inhabitants by name, and also knew exactly what was happening in each house, not only because she had been right there from the beginning, but because her house was in the middle of the village and everyone loved to visit. Dropped in for tea. Shared their news. Cried on her shoulder. Aunt Lovey was such a plump and comforting presence, like a warm eiderdown, that people would tell her things. Secrets. And she would hold their hands and never scold, and never judge. She would just sit and listen and look at them with her soft, kind eyes.

Aunt Lovey's eyes were like the inside of a perlemoen shell. They were blue and green and aquamarine all at once, and when she heard a sad story they would grow misty, like the sea. Sometimes they would fill with tears, and I swear her tears were like drops from a rainbow, running down her plump, powdered cheeks from the corners of those mother-of-pearl eyes. I have never seen eyes like that since, but when I come across a perlemoen shell on a beach, I feel I am looking into them again.

Aunt Lovey's yellow-brown hair was thick and wavy and she wore it in a plait coiled on the top of her head, like a rope of butterscotch toffee. Sometimes, strands of the plait would work loose and hang down, all spangled with hairpins. They would drop down her neck or into her bosom and she would grab a fly swatter and clap it on her shoulders so that the hairpins would clatter onto the stoep on either side of her chair. '*Ag,* such useless thingamabobs.'

And when I crouched down to pick them up she would swish her skirt to one side in order to help me find them.

Aunt Lovey held her skirts in place by tying a bright sash very tightly round her middle, with a floppy bow at the back. And being so short and plump, the tight sashes would push her top up and her bottom down, so that she seemed to come in two halves, like a cottage loaf. Her shoes were tightly laced and flat, with rounded toes like polished pebbles. They caused her to tripple a little, from side to side, when she walked.

Trippling along, always smiling, arms stretched out in welcome, perfumed with lavender and a hint of buchu – that's how I remember her. If I shut my eyes I can see her precisely.

The first time she told me a story was when, having finished my homework one afternoon,

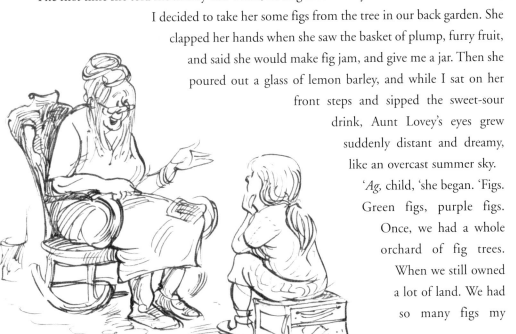

I decided to take her some figs from the tree in our back garden. She clapped her hands when she saw the basket of plump, furry fruit, and said she would make fig jam, and give me a jar. Then she poured out a glass of lemon barley, and while I sat on her front steps and sipped the sweet-sour drink, Aunt Lovey's eyes grew suddenly distant and dreamy, like an overcast summer sky.

'*Ag,* child, 'she began. 'Figs. Green figs, purple figs. Once, we had a whole orchard of fig trees. When we still owned a lot of land. We had so many figs my mother used to invite all the farmer's wives over for a day to come and make jam and preserve, and the kitchen would be full of figs and sugar and bubbling pots and noisy women. *Tannies.*

Oh, there was terrible steam and noise and my mother hadn't any time for me then. They were so busy that no one took any notice of me, so one day I picked up a hat belonging to Aunt Sarie from Wilgersfontein. It was lying on a chair in the hall, a big bonnet with flowers in the front, and I turned it upside down and poured a jar of hot preserve into it. And then I just stood there in the middle of the kitchen, waiting.'

Aunt Lovey shook with laughter as she remembered the scene. 'Goodness child, how those ladies screamed! They all turned from their jobs, looked at me, and screamed. So I turned the bonnet upside down and the soft, syrupy figs plopped all over the kitchen floor. Tant Sarie ran to pick up her bonnet, slipped on the figs and fell flat on her back. Out came such a hiccup, it was like a balloon bursting. She was hefty too, a really big lady, and it took three of them to help her stand up again. My mother took me to my bedroom, banged the door shut, sat me on the bed and bent over with laughter.'

'"That was wicked," she said, holding her hand to her mouth so that the laughter wouldn't come through, only the words, hoping that the ladies in the kitchen were listening. "You're a very naughty girl. Into bed with you, and no supper tonight."'

Aunt Lovey's chair shook now as she laughed, its rockers going screech-clop on the stone stoep. 'Yes, figs. Thank you child. You must come again.'

'Thank you Aunt Lovey, I will.'

And I did, and that was the beginning of the Corriebush stories. The telling took many years. At first Aunt Lovey was very careful about how much she would tell a child, and she edited her stories with great care. For years she told me only the funny ones, over and over; stories devoid of any bad language – or worse – sexual capers. But as I grew older she became more daring, letting me into darker secrets, although she never referred to sensitive matters in plain language. 'A little bit of foxtrot' meant there was something sexy involved. 'A hand in the biscuit tin' meant someone had stolen something. Aunt Lovey was simply too good a person to gossip, and she left it to me, as I grew older and more mature, to read the adult meanings into her words.

By the time I left Corriebush at the age of twenty-two, I was able to piece each story together. Fill in the gaps. They had taken many years in the telling and if I get stuck now, when writing this, I need only shut my eyes and travel back again to Aunt Lovey's stoep.

'Tell me the story again about Sannie and the flags.'

'Then bring me my spectacles, child.'

When Aunt Lovey told a story she always wore her spectacles. She never looked through them, she always looked over the top, letting them sit on her nose. Spectacles in place, she would smooth her skirt over her plump knees, lean back in her rocker until it creaked, tip her head and look through the fanlight in the corrugated-iron roof.

Then her eyes would mist over and she would sigh. '*Ag,* child.' (Even when I had come of age, she still called me child.) 'Here, take a biscuit. You see, it happened like this.'

Sometimes the story took weeks to finish, but I never pressed her. I knew when she was tired, and I would go home then and write it all down and not tell anyone. Not until now. For Aunt Lovey has gone, and all the people she told me about – they, too, have gone.

But perhaps their ghosts still wander about Corriebush, for it's a place that is not easy to leave or forget.

BETSIE

When Betsie de Waal told her parents that she had been invited to The Annual Stockfair Ball they were delighted. Betsie was Hendrik and Gertie's only child. A fine woman, a devoted daughter and a cause of great anxiety to her parents.

'Thirty years old and no man has ever looked at her. It breaks a mother's heart,' Gertie often sighed.

The women of Corriebush regularly discussed the subject at their tea parties. Match-making was of deep concern to them, and Betsie's case was of great importance. Because they were naturally gentle, kindly women, they were reluctant to put the truth about Betsie into words. Instead, they pretended to be totally puzzled, clicking their tongues and frowning into their cups.

'Such a lovely nature. So friendly. Always ready with a smile and a little joke. Capable too! No one can bake like Betsie can.'

And then one afternoon, Nellie lost patience with all the sweet talk and spoke bluntly.

'Come now. We all know that Betsie is a good and honest woman, but she *is* rather hefty, and has absolutely no feminine tricks. And a man – being the silly creature he is – likes a woman who will tease him a little, flutter her eyelashes, play with her necklace, that sort of thing.'

Anna found her tongue. 'You're right, Nellie. When it comes to flirting, Betsie doesn't have the faintest. Never mind the necklaces.'

'Hands like spades and walks like a farmer,' put in Lily.

'Huge strides and big feet. You can hear her coming down the street before she's even out of the bakkie, poor child.'

'It's because she grew up helping Hendrik on the land. Driving tractors, fixing windmills, they say she can even shear a sheep. Out in all weathers too, no wonder her skin looks like it does.'

Sophia shifted uneasily, thinking they were being a bit harsh.

'Well you can't expect a young woman to work like a carthorse and look like the Queen of England, can you?'

'No,' Anna conceded. 'And of course her hair is beautiful.'

And indeed it was. A waterfall that hung to her waist. Thick and curly, and an astonishing red, shot with gold. Left to itself, Betsie could have worn it like a cloak, but she said it got in the way, reminded her of an Angora goat, and so wore it scraped back and tightly plaited.

'I was visiting once when she was getting ready for bed and came to say goodnight to her parents. Her hair was loose and she wore a white nightdress and I tell you, she looked like a fairytale, if you know what I mean.'

'What I can't understand is how Hendrik and Gertie are happy with it all.'

'With what all?'

'Her planting potatoes and so on.'

Truth was, they weren't. They would have been so delighted to have their daughter sitting quietly at home sewing, perhaps preparing a trousseau. Of course Hendrik did appreciate her help, especially not having a son and him getting on in years, and Gertie was equally grateful for Betsie's help in the kitchen and the wonderful meals she prepared.

'We must be thankful for her energy and devotion,' they often told each other. 'But what will happen when we pass on one day? She can't stay here alone on the farm.'

It was a real problem. And so when Betsie came with the news that she had been invited to The Ball, they were truly thrilled.

'And who,' beamed Hendrik, 'is the lucky man?'

Betsie guessed what their reaction would be, so she answered defiantly, for so good-natured a daughter.

'Hamish McAndrew!'

Hendrik leapt up as though she'd thrown a snake in his lap and Gertie burst into tears.

Hamish McAndrew was a Scot who farmed in the district, and the fact that he had never been accepted by the community was altogether his fault.

The Corriebush townsfolk and farmers always made an effort to welcome newcomers. So they had visited Hamish, bearing bottles of brandy, freshly baked pies and jars of preserves. Then, having paid their respects, they had naturally discussed him. And all had agreed that Hamish McAndrew was 'a funny man'.

'Gruff,' one of them noted. 'Didn't even ask us inside.'

'Us neither,' another chimed in.

'Polite enough, though, took the roast chicken and said thank you very much. Definitely a foreign accent. Must be descended from one of those interfering Scottish missionaries who came out in the last century.'

'Well, what I say is why does a man come here without a family, buy a farm, live there alone, not talking much and no curtains even? Did you notice that?'

'He needs a woman. But with that moustache?'

'Quite handsome, though, in a way,' Lily conceded. 'Big, strong man. But what does he know about sheep, I wonder?'

In time, however, they grew used to Hamish. He would attend stockfairs and pay good prices, cash, for sheep and cattle, and he always returned their greetings and doffed his broad-brimmed hat. But, having bought his stock, he would climb into his bakkie and drive off back to his farm, never taking time to pass the time of day. Their daughters, always on the look-out for a husband when a new man arrived in the district, soon gave up.

'A lost cause,' they decided.

And then Hamish asked Betsie to The Ball. Walked right up to where she was standing in the Corner Shop one Saturday morning, having come to town for provisions, and without lowering his voice he issued the invitation. Betsie blushed, and accepted, and that was that.

'No good will come of this,' Gertie told Hendrik after they had both calmed down. 'But what can we do?'

In a way she was half relieved that Betsie had been noticed, but one thing could lead to another.

'What if they get married, Hendrik? Our Betsie to a Scot? The man's not one of us. After all, what does he know about the Great Trek? And Piet Retief?'

'Don't be silly old woman. It's just a dance.'

Every year, everyone in Corriebush and the district went to The Ball. The husbands and fathers, the wives and mothers sat on chairs around the perimeter of the dance floor and watched while their daughters – in their long, full-skirted dresses of lace and tulle – swirled around the floor to the waltz and the foxtrot, with plenty of Paul Jones' in between.

Betsie wore a long, pink dress with rosebuds and puffed sleeves, her red mop swept up in a ribbon, and everyone agreed that she looked surprisingly attractive.

Hamish wore a tartan kilt. They were shocked. Betsie did not seem to mind that his legs were showing, and it had to be said that he really could waltz. His back was straight, his dark hair smoothly sleeked, his moustache waxed and twirled. He even smiled at her as they swept around the room. And Betsie was gone.

It was a quiet wedding, no fuss, because Hendrik was struggling a bit, and no honeymoon. They went straight to Hamish's farm, Sweetwater, after the ceremony. And overnight, as it were, Betsie became a new woman.

'Never known anyone to change like that,' the women remarked, after visiting. 'She's even wearing rouge.'

'And high heels.'

'Perfume too. She's still our Betsie, but she certainly is different.'

'She's quite the lady now. You can be sure she won't be working on the land anymore.'

'And did you see the curtains she's made? I didn't even know Betsie could sew.'

It was all true. Betsie had emerged like a butterfly from a pupa and in no time transformed the dull, dreary house into a comfortable home. It was still sparsely furnished – Hamish had been a bachelor for a long time – but there were cushions on the chairs now and flowers in the vases and the kitchen was always dense with the aroma of baking.

Betsie was delighted when the women came to call. If she looked through the window and saw a puff of dust on the road leading up to the farm, she would blush with excitement.

'Visitors!' she would call to Hamish as the car clunked over the cattle grid and stopped in the yard, the driver giving a loud blast on the hooter. She would tear off her apron, pat her hair, and run out to meet them. The women always shrieked and hugged and talked all the way up the steps and into the house, and Betsie would rush straight to the kitchen to see to tea. They all helped her lay the cloth on the dining-room table, put out the cups and carry the cakes through before settling down to talk.

Betsie would never pour until her husband was seated at the head of the table. Having taken his place, Hamish would sit there in silence and utter dismay. His farm was going to hell.

The reasons for his marrying Betsie had become a little blurred over the last few months because he had grown so fond of her. His wife was so sweet-natured and cared for him so lovingly, prepared such delicious meals and had made his place so homely that somewhere at the back of his mind, in moments of total honesty, feelings of guilt were surfacing. He had married her simply because he hoped that she would pull his farm together. Now he was ashamed of himself. Betsie couldn't be both on the land and in the house, the rains hadn't come, the farm was actually going backwards, and he had run out of money.

'Would you rather have her on a tractor in dirty overalls then?' he sometimes asked himself.

The answer was no, but he was anxious and confused, and so he sat sullenly through the tea parties, brooding and glowering.

They wondered why he didn't leave and go outside. They didn't know that he stayed because the gossip and frivolity took him away from Outside. Outside was nothing but a space of depression. The veld was dry, the stock were thin, and the bushes munched down to brittle grey cobwebs. So he would stay, and blow on his tea, and say nothing, and sometimes Betsie would put her hand in front of her mouth and say in an aside, '*Ag*, he's a bit shy, you know. Don't worry, it's nothing.'

'It isn't nothing,' Anna often said darkly on the way home. 'We should have warned her. Better have stayed on the shelf than marry a closed book.'

'Yes, and did you see how he frowns over his tea cup? Looks such a thundercloud I get quite frightened,' admitted Nellie.

'But then another day I swear I saw him wink at her.'

'And yet she doesn't look unhappy. Perhaps it's a game they're playing.'

Sophia had the last word. 'You never know what happens in the bedroom.'

What happened in the bedroom was a little bit of foxtrot and, when Betsie fell pregnant, Hamish boarded a mailship and went to Scotland.

'He says there's family money there,' Betsie told them. 'Says he wants to provide properly for his son. Send him to school in England. Nothing but the best. He'll be back soon, don't worry.'

But Betsie *did* worry. Hamish was not a good farmer, and she suspected that he was in debt, but he had never ever mentioned any family fortune overseas.

'Why don't you just go back to your parents, Betsie?' Nellie asked her, a question which made her quite angry.

'Because I really care about him! He gave me his name, made me a woman, never raised a hand to me.'

'But what will you do, Bets, if he doesn't return?'

'He will. When he left here he didn't know it, but there was a lock of my hair in his sporran.'

Sophia let out a gasp. 'In his *what*?'

'His sporran. He'll come back. I'm not worried.'

If Betsie had looked into Hamish's bank balance, she would have been very worried. If she had known that he had not set foot in Scotland since had he visited with his father at the age of seven, that he knew of no living relatives, and that he had sailed away in a desperate effort to find a way out of the situation because he really cared deeply about her and his child – if she had known the extent of his hopelessness she would have been very worried indeed.

Hamish had plenty of time to think on the long voyage to Southampton, and once the ship had docked he wasted no time in heading directly north. Even though he had been so young when he had visited Scotland with his father, he had a clear image of his grandparent's cottage in a small fishing village on the west coast, and as the train rattled across the Highlands to Kyle of Lochalsh, he realised he could not be far wrong, because everything looked so familiar: the fierce, craggy mountains, the clumps of yellow gorse, the rushing brown streams and long-haired cattle. He'd been here before, and all he had to do was to walk a few miles up the coast from Kyle, and he was sure he would find the place. And he did, arriving in the late afternoon on a wild, wet winter's day.

'McAndrew?' the postmaster shook his head. 'Buried long ago, son. Don't know if there's any family left, or where they went. But go and ask at the pub. If any man knows, you'll be sure to find him in there.'

'McAndrew? You a McAndrew? First one I've seen in many a year. None of them left in these parts. All gone now. But where you come from, lad?'

Old Jock gave a roar of surprise and slapped his glass down, leaving a pool of whisky on the polished counter. He wiped it with his sleeve. 'Africa? Africa you say? Hoots mon, you'll be needing a stiff drink then. Come on chaps, all chuck in, a double drink on the house for this fellow, he's come a long way, he has.'

One drink led to another, as each man in the pub stood Hamish a round.

'Tell us about the crocodiles, Mac. I hear they're as big as submarines!' and Hamish would make up a story.

'And the elephants? They say Africa *crawls* with elephants!'

'And snakes as thick as a caber.'

Lots of stories, until Hamish was so befuddled he forgot his pride and told them the truth. He was one of them, a Scot, down on his luck with a run-down farm and a pregnant wife and he was looking for money.

Well now, they didn't give money away, they said, but they would take him on a bet.

'You lose, you're done for. You win, and we'll pass the hat. Fifty pound from every man here if you spend one night alone in Locharney Castle.'

The men nodded eagerly.

'Alone lad, but for the ghosts!'

'The last fellow went stark mad and he's still in chains somewhere!'

'*Och* come now Jock, can't you see the poor chap's not fit for it?'

Hamish drained his glass. 'Done!' he said.

Locharney Castle stood on the very edge of a cliff facing the Outer Hebrides. Built in the 15th century by the wealthy head of a noble clan, the castle was once surrounded by gardens and fountains, the interior filled with carved oak furniture, suits of armour, flamboyant tapestries – all the riches of an ancestral home. But when Joshua McTavish fell off his horse and subsequently died from his injuries, his wife, the Honourable Lady Eleanor McTavish, grieved until she lost her mind, and her relatives put her away somewhere.

The castle stood empty. Over the years the whipping salt spray and vicious winds mercilessly raked the castle, battering the stately ramparts into grotesque shapes, like broken teeth. The garden soon became a swamp, and all the magnificent treasures disappeared from inside. All that remained was the vast entrance hall, the solid, sweeping staircase, and the shattered upper gallery.

'G'bye laddie!' they called as they shot the bolt in the massive front door and left Hamish standing, a little unsteadily, at the foot of the staircase in the dark.

Groping, he found the banister and sat down on the first step. He was suddenly stone-cold sober. He shivered. On either side of the door were tall, domed windows, empty of glass, and an icy rain was driving in, making pools on the stone floor and bulleting against the walls. Outside, the wind howled and shrieked and threw itself against the old ruin, bent on flattening it, tumbling stone upon stone.

Behind Hamish the stairs creaked. He turned and saw, through the arrow slit on the landing, the palest of moons briefly shafting through the clouds. It caught the bare branches of a tree and threw dancing skeletons on the wall. Then it was pitch dark again. An owl hooted nearby, its drowsy call half-suffocated by the gale. And then suddenly the wind dropped. The rain stopped. The castle shuddered and sighed, and then the night became dead still. It was hideous.

From somewhere above the step on which Hamish sat came a frantic, scratching noise. Then a soft shuffling. Muffled sniffing. Something, someone, was coming down the stairs, and the black silence was broken by a terrible, terrifying scream. When Hamish tried to stand up, he realised that the scream was his, and he was surrounded by rats. Snuffling, scurrying, enormous rats. He was sober enough by now to feel ashamed.

'Coward!' he shouted out loud, kicking at the creatures. 'What on earth would Betsie say?'

Slowly he climbed the steps and went to sleep on the smooth, flat landing.

Next morning was calm and sunny, birds were singing, a few had flown in and were drinking from the pools of water still on the floor. Hamish stood up, stretched, and slowly started down the grand old staircase. He had stayed the night, won the bet, and he held his head high. He could not know that his hair had turned snow white.

The key turned in the great brass lock, and Jock flung the door wide open. 'Well now, lad! Looks as though you made it! A whole night alone in haunted old Locharney. But hang on a minute, fellow! Hang on! Not alone are we?' Jock was looking past Hamish's shoulder.

'Who is the red-headed lass standing quietly behind ye?'

'And that,' Hamish said, 'is the whole story, Bets. I'm so happy to be home again. Now show me the wee lad.'

Betsie took his hand, leading the way. 'He's got bright red hair,' she smiled back at him.

Hamish had come away with one thousand pounds in bet money. He was able to re-fence and restock his farm, and bought a house, Number One, in Corriebush. Hendrik sold his farm and he and Gertie moved in to Number One, keeping an eye on the place, and paying Hamish a small rent. And when they passed on, Hamish and Betsie moved to town and retired to Number One, leaving an expanded and prospering Sweetwater to their three fine red-headed sons.

The women of Corriebush, a good bit older now, were jubilant.

'We must eat our words,' said Maria.

'What a fine man after all,' proclaimed Lily.

'Just goes to show, life is full of surprises.'

They sat on Anna's stoep, smiling rather smugly, while Maria carefully divided, into six slices, the Dundee cake Betsie had brought them for tea.

BETSIE'S RECIPES

When it came to cooking and baking, Betsie had a foot in two camps. Her skills and natural preference lay in the foods she had enjoyed since childhood – the roasted Karoo lamb, the sweet heavy puddings, and the tea-time bakes for which farmers' wives were justly famous. Her marriage to Hamish presented a real challenge. Scottish food was absolutely foreign to her, but in a flush of eagerness to please her husband, she hunted down a book of international recipes in the Corriebush library, and set about experimenting with this new cuisine.

After a disastrous fiddle with a sheep's paunch and pluck, Betsie begged off haggis, and Hamish stepped in to help. Scottish women, he told her, had a flair not only for baking (think cakes and scones and shortbread) but also for making the best of whatever ingredients were at hand – good stuff like prime beef, Highland honey, oatmeal in abundance, and chunky root vegetables for hearty soups.

Betsie learnt quickly, adapted where necessary, and was soon able to serve reasonably authentic, wholesome meals. The baking side was easy. This was familiar territory for her, and in no time she was able to lay on a traditional Scottish tea when the women came to call. But she really was happiest dipping into both cuisines, with broths and bredies, oatcakes and *oblietjies* mingling like old friends on her table.

The women were impressed. 'No flies on our Betsie,' was their unanimous verdict. 'Always rises to the occasion like a good loaf of bread.'

Mushroom, Leek and Barley Broth

The title may sound pedestrian, but this is a soup unlike any other:
earthy and intense, with a slightly smoky fragrance, it is quite different
from the usual creamy mushroom soups. This version requires the mushrooms
to 'mull' for an hour or so in red wine, while the colour and flavour gather depth.
The addition of leeks and barley gives a nod to Scotland, the quince jelly adds a surprising
local touch, and the final blend is simply a lovely comfort soup for a chilly night.

125 ml (½ cup) pearled barley
2 medium onions, finely chopped
4 large leeks, shredded
60 ml (4 Tbsp) butter
2 medium carrots, finely diced
500 g brown mushrooms,
wiped and chopped
250 ml (1 cup) red wine
(claret is a good choice)
5 ml (1 tsp) grated nutmeg
2 litres (8 cups) chicken stock*
20 ml (4 tsp) tomato paste
sea salt to taste
20 ml (4 tsp) quince jelly
a little chopped parsley

* Next time you roast a chicken,
make a stock from the
carcass – a home-made stock
makes all the difference here.

Rinse the barley and soak in water to cover for 45 minutes. Meanwhile, place the onions, leeks, butter, carrots, mushrooms, wine and nutmeg in a large, deep saucepan. Bring to the boil, then cook briskly, uncovered, stirring until the liquid has reduced to a few bubbles and the vegetables start to darken. Now add the stock, tomato paste, salt and the drained barley and, when boiling, reduce the heat, cover and simmer gently for at least 1 hour, stirring now and then. Check the seasoning, swirl in the jelly and parsley, then leave the soup to stand for 10 minutes before serving, while it thickens to maximum, and all the flavours come together. Ladle into warmed, deep bowls. **Serves 8.**

Butternut and Sweet Potato Soup

The addition of fresh ginger at the end adds an elusive zing to this gently glowing old favourite.

15 ml (1 Tbsp) oil
a small knob of butter
1 large onion, finely chopped
2 ml (½ tsp) each grated nutmeg,
ground cinnamon and turmeric
500 g butternut, peeled and diced
(prepared weight)
250 g peeled, diced, red-skinned
sweet potatoes (prepared weight)
2 medium Golden Delicious apples,
peeled and diced
1 litre (4 cups) hot chicken or
vegetable stock
2 bay leaves
sea salt to taste
30 ml (2 Tbsp) coarsely grated,
peeled root ginger
250 ml (1 cup) milk
lemon juice and honey (optional)
thin cream (optional)

Heat the oil and butter in a large saucepan, add the onion and, when turning golden, add the spices, tossing until aromatic. As the spices usually absorb excess oil, add a little water so that they can announce their flavour without scorching – keep the heat low. Add the vegetables and apples, and toss to mix them with the spices and to colour them a little, then add the stock, bay leaves and salt. (This quantity of liquid may seem very little, but the apples add their juices and there's still some milk to come.) Cover and simmer very gently until everything is soft – about 25 minutes – adding the ginger a few minutes before the end of the cooking period. Leave to cool before removing the bay leaves, then purée the soup in a blender until absolutely smooth; you will need to do this in two or more batches. Return to the saucepan, stir in the milk, and taste – it might need more salt, a dash of lemon juice, or even a trickle of honey. Reheat, stirring. If you are making the soup in advance, don't reheat – pour into a suitable container with a lid and refrigerate overnight. To serve, pour the hot soup into heated soup bowls. It would be a pity to mask the spicy character with a flavoursome garnish, but a cobweb of thin cream in the centre of each serving is good. Just drop in a teaspoonful and swirl the cream around with a skewer. **Serves 8.**

CURRY-BUTTER JACKET POTATOES

A deliciously different way of treating new potatoes.
Nicely spiced and prettily glossed, they team up perfectly with roast chicken.
Add cinnamon-baked pumpkin and a green veg for a rustic meal with traditional flavours.

750 g (11–12) new potatoes*
15 ml (1 Tbsp) each oil and butter
20 ml (4 tsp) curry powder**
2 ml (½ tsp) turmeric
250 ml (1 cup) hot chicken or
vegetable stock
a little sea salt
15 ml (1 Tbsp) smooth fruit chutney
a fistful of fresh coriander leaves
30 ml (2 Tbsp) butter
a trickle of honey

* Use new potatoes of the same size
– approximately that of an XL egg.
** If possible, buy a top quality, pure
curry powder with coarsely
ground spices, e.g. Cape Malay
Curry Powder.

Scrub the potatoes well and jab them once or twice, quite deeply, with the point of a sharp knife, then set aside. Heat the oil and butter in a frying pan large enough to hold the potatoes in a single layer. Add the curry powder and turmeric, and stir for a few seconds over low heat before adding the potatoes. Toss them around until they're coated with the spices (add a dash of water if too dry), then add the stock and salt – just a little, as the stock will be salty if not home-made. Cover and simmer until cooked (test with the tip of a knife) – keep the heat low so that the liquid does not boil away. When done, use a slotted spoon to transfer the potatoes to a warmed serving dish. Add the chutney, coriander, butter and honey (to taste) to the pan juices, and stir until mixed and heated through. Pour the sauce over the potatoes, toss, and serve. Or, if you're not ready to serve, return the potatoes to the pan and keep them warm until the main course is ready, in which case you might need to add a dash more stock. **Serves 5–6.**

Venison Stew with Allesverloren and Prunes

In the old days in the Karoo, game was marinated for days before cooking it, to tone down the gamey, outright hairy flavour. But that was then. Now, with butchers selling farm-reared, young springbok, it's a different story – marinating is often skipped, and fillets and steaks served rare. Not so in this dish, in which the rules are bent, and steaks are given the old-fashioned treatment – a slow, well-done simmer. The result is fabulous: soft, tender chunks of meat in a richly flavoured gravy, glossed with jelly. This is stove-top cooking, which means you can check and stir whenever necessary, and it can all be done in advance – in fact it's even more delicious the next day. Serve with clapshot – a weird and wonderful name for a simple dish of mash from the chilly islands to the north of Scotland. There, it is usually served with sausages, but it goes very well with this venison stew, and makes a welcome change from the traditional yellow rice.

4 x 200 g boneless venison steaks from a young springbok leg
30 ml (2 Tbsp) red wine vinegar
150 g pitted prunes, halved
100 ml (⅖ cup) Allesverloren port
oil and butter for browning
2 large onions, finely chopped
4 rashers unsmoked back bacon, diced
2 medium carrots, diced
30 ml (2 Tbsp) flour
600 ml (2⅖ cups) hot, seasoned beef stock
60 ml (¼ cup) extra port
15 ml (1 Tbsp) tomato paste
Spices and seasoning: 3 whole cloves, 2 bay leaves, 2 sticks cinnamon, a large pinch of ground allspice, 2 x 5 cm strips lemon peel, and a little sea salt
15 ml (1 Tbsp) quince jelly

Using a sharp knife, pull off any thin membrane round the steaks. Pour the vinegar into a glass dish, add the steaks, turn over and over until coated, and leave for 1–2 hours. Place the prunes in a shallow dish and cover with the port. Wipe the steaks dry and slice each into 3–4 chunks. Heat the oil and butter in a really large, wide saucepan and brown the meat well on both sides, then remove and set aside. Reduce the heat, add a little extra oil to the pan, then add the onions, bacon and carrots and, when soft and golden, sprinkle in the flour. When absorbed, stir in the stock, extra port, tomato paste and all the spices and seasoning. Return the meat to the saucepan, cover, and simmer over *low* heat for 1 hour, then stir in the prunes and port, and simmer for another 30 minutes. Finally, stir in the jelly to work its magic. Serve immediately or cool, turn into a suitable container, and refrigerate overnight. Add a little extra stock if necessary to thin out the gravy. **Serves 4–5.**

Clapshot

300 g turnips, peeled and sliced
(prepared weight)
500 g potatoes, peeled and cubed
(prepared weight)
30 ml (2 Tbsp) butter
15 ml (1 Tbsp) oil
3 medium leeks, shredded
a pinch of grated nutmeg
sea salt and white pepper to taste
warm milk

Choose medium rather than very large turnips for this dish. Once prepared, cook in a little boiling salted water for 15 minutes. Add the potatoes and boil together until both vegetables are soft, adding a little extra water if necessary. Meanwhile, heat the butter and oil in a medium frying pan and sauté the leeks gently until soft and golden. Drain excess water from the cooked turnips and potatoes, return to the pot and add the leeks and any buttery pan juices, together with the nutmeg and seasoning. Mash everything together with a little milk to make it creamy.

Tomato Bobotie

This recipe, without being hostile to tradition, does differ slightly from the regular version, and the result is a soft, succulent and exceptionally *lekker* bobotie.

1 medium-thick slice crustless bread
375 ml (1½ cups) milk
(low-fat if preferred)
30 ml (2 Tbsp) oil
2 medium onions, finely chopped
about 20 ml (4 tsp) coarsely grated,
peeled root ginger
3 cloves garlic, crushed
45 ml (3 Tbsp) medium curry powder
5 ml (1 tsp) turmeric
1 kg lean beef mince,
preferably free-range
45 ml (3 Tbsp) smooth, mild chutney
30 ml (2 Tbsp) smooth apricot jam
60 ml (4 Tbsp) seedless raisins
about 10 ml (2 tsp) sea salt
1 apple, peeled and coarsely grated
(preferably Golden Delicious)
200 ml (⅘ cup) tomato purée
1 large free-range egg, beaten
a good squeeze of fresh lemon juice

TOPPING
2 large free-range eggs, turmeric,
salt, bay leaves and toasted
flaked almonds

Soak the bread in the milk. Heat the oil in a large, deep saucepan or frying pan and gently fry the onions, ginger and garlic. Add the curry powder and turmeric and toss for a minute, then add the mince. Toss – don't stir – over low heat until the meat is a uniform yellow-brown – no pink should remain. If necessary, add a dash of water to prevent the spices from scorching and to loosen the mixture. Add the remaining bobotie ingredients, including the squeezed-dry bread – reserve the milk. Mix well, then turn into a lightly oiled baking dish, about 30 x 20 cm – the mixture should be roughly 3 cm deep. Smooth evenly. Bake at 180 °C for 30 minutes.

For the topping, beat the eggs with the reserved milk (make up to 300 ml (1⅕ cups) if necessary) adding a good pinch of turmeric and salt. Carefully pour over the meat mixture, slip in a few bay leaves, and scatter with almonds. Reduce the heat to 160 °C and bake for 40–45 minutes until set. **Serves 8.**

Spiced Brandied Peaches

So as not to mask the fabulous flavour of one of summer's most luscious fruits –
plump, glowing, freestone peaches – they are poached in a syrup that is only
lightly spiced and only slightly tipsy. Chilled for a day or two and served with
pouring cream or vanilla ice cream, this is an old favourite that will never lose its appeal.

250 ml (1 cup) water
1 stick cinnamon
2 whole cloves
150 ml (⅗ cup) light brown sugar
45 ml (3 Tbsp) brandy
6 large, firm but ripe freestone peaches (900 g–1 kg)
extra brandy
a few drops of vanilla essence

Prepare the syrup by bringing the water, spices, sugar and brandy to the boil in a large frying pan, stirring until the sugar has dissolved, then set aside. To prepare the peaches, run a knife round each, from top to bottom, and give a twist to separate the halves. Remove the pip and, if the peach is properly ripe, it will be easy to pull off the skin. If this proves difficult, peel it thinly and smoothly. Place the peaches, hollows down, in the syrup, and poach, covered, until just tender (test with a skewer); if they are ripe, this should take only 10–15 minutes. Cool in the syrup, remove the whole spices, then use a slotted spoon to transfer the peaches to a deep, wide serving dish, large enough to hold them in a single layer. Have a sip of the syrup, add a little more brandy if necessary and a few drops of vanilla, then pour it over the peaches – they should be almost submerged. Refrigerate, covered, for up to 2 days. **Serves 6.**

Poached Naartjies Van der Hum

Naartjies are no longer what they used to be. These days they come with a peel
that peels clean off without any snags, and no pips. These are the ones to use
for this easy but ambrosial dessert in which the fruit nestles in a light caramel sauce
spiked with Van der Hum liqueur. Once poached and chilled, the segments are delicious
spooned over ice cream – especially vanilla or mango. They need to be prepared in
advance – even a day before needed. A sprinkling of candied orange peel is optional,
but contrasts well with the soft, sweet naartjies.

500 ml (2 cups) water
250 ml (1 cup) light brown sugar
650 g naartjie segments (prepared weight)*
1 stick cinnamon
60 ml (¼ cup) Van der Hum liqueur

* Whole, poached naartjies look grander, but they do tend to fall apart very easily; using segments is flop-proof.

Bring the water and sugar to a slow boil in a large, wide-based frying pan, stirring to dissolve the sugar completely. Add the naartjie segments and the cinnamon, then reduce the heat and simmer gently for about 20 minutes, or until the segments are really soft and plump, stirring gently once or twice. Don't cover the saucepan during poaching, just tilt the lid a little. Using a slotted spoon, carefully transfer the fruit to a heatproof dish (as you're shortly going to douse it with hot syrup). Remove the cinnamon from the syrup and then boil rapidly until very bubbly, reduced and a *pale* caramel in colour. Don't go further than pale – a darker caramel will settle into toffee as it cools. You will need about 250 ml (1 cup) syrup; if necessary, spoon off any excess. Stir in the liqueur and pour the syrup over the naartjies. Baste a few times as they cool, then cover and chill. **Serves 6.**

Candied orange peel

In a small saucepan, dissolve 45 ml (3 Tbsp) light brown sugar in 30 ml (2 Tbsp) water. Add the thinly julienned peel (without a trace of pith) of one small orange, simmer for a few minutes until bubbly and starting to caramelize, then remove and carefully stir in 30 ml (2 Tbsp) water. Leave to cool and soften in the syrup. Drain before using.

Lemon and Almond Shortbread Fingers

Melt-in-the-mouth, buttery shortbread is an integral part of any Highland tea, and as traditional as haggis and oats. Nevertheless, the ingredients and the methods used for making shortbread are not absolutely rigid and – as in Betsie's case – it is never wise to try to make something 'exactly like mother used to bake'. Here are two variations: Lemon and Almond Fingers, and Brown Walnut Wedges. Different in both flavour and shape, they are equally delicious.

250 g butter (at room temperature), cubed
finely grated rind of 1 large lemon
125 ml (½ cup) castor sugar
600 ml (2⅖ cups) cake flour
150 ml (⅗ cup) cornflour*
60–75 ml (4–5 Tbsp) flaked almonds, lightly toasted
about 5 ml (1 tsp) castor sugar for dusting

* Rice flour is traditional, but not readily available in South Africa – cornflour makes a good substitute.
** The size of the baking sheet is important – no larger, or the shortbread will be too thin.

Place the butter and lemon rind in a large mixing bowl. (Use a big, thick-skinned, well-washed lemon, and be careful not to include any of the pith when grating.) Using an electric whisk, cream these well, then slowly beat in the castor sugar until the mixture is fluffy and pale yellow. Sift the flour with the cornflour and add gradually, beating well, until the mixture is moist and finely crumbed, then use your hands to knead until the mixture comes together in a smooth, putty-like ball. Finally, knead in the almonds. Line a 26 x 20 cm** baking sheet with baking paper, and press the mixture in firmly and as evenly as possible. Use a fork to prick the mixture all over, and mark lightly into 24 fingers. Bake on the middle shelf of the oven at 160 °C for 10 minutes, then reduce the heat to 150 °C and bake for a further 50 minutes. When done, the shortbread should be a rich blonde colour, never browned. Remove from the oven and carefully cut through the fingers. Sprinkle with castor sugar, then leave on the sheet until absolutely cold before removing. **Makes 24 fingers.**

Brown Walnut Shortbread Wedges

Wholewheat flour makes a deliciously crunchy shortbread, and it's a tad more
wholesome than the blonde variety. Use plain brown bread flour if preferred,
it works just as well. If you wish to make a larger batch, the method remains the same,
but double the ingredients, use a lined 26 x 20 cm baking tin,
and score into fingers – this will give you 24.

250 ml (1 cup) wholewheat or
plain brown bread flour
125 ml (½ cup) cornflour
a wee pinch of salt
60 ml (¼ cup) castor sugar
125 g soft butter, cubed
60 ml (¼ cup) finely chopped walnuts
icing sugar for dusting

Sift the flour, cornflour and salt into a mixing bowl, adding any bran left in the sieve. Mix in the castor sugar, rub in the butter, then knead until the mixture binds and forms a smooth ball. Knead in the walnuts. Line the base of a shallow, 19 cm cake tin with baking paper, and press the mixture in evenly. Prick all over, and pretty up round the edge with the tines of a fork, then score lightly into 8 wedges. Bake at 160 °C for 10 minutes, then reduce the heat to 150 °C and bake for a further 50–55 minutes. Unlike shortbread using cake flour, brown flour shortbread will be beige to light brown in colour. Cut through the wedges, leave in the tin until cold, sift over a little icing sugar (this is simply to jolly up the rather dull colour) and remove. Store in an airtight container with a little sugar sprinkled on the bottom to keep the shortbread crisp.
Makes 8 large wedges.

Farmhouse Finger Rusks with Buttermilk and Oats

Early morning coffee with dunking rusks is so much a Karoo tradition.
The old-fashioned method of kneading and balling is probably the most popular,
but it is time-consuming. This version is good and wholesome and much quicker –
the soft, sticky dough is simply turned into a loaf tin (for a loaf of rusks)
or a rectangular tin (for a flattish slab). Once baked, they are cooled, turned out,
and cut into fingers. And you can make them with only white flour, only bran-rich flour,
half white and half bran-rich, or in any proportion you like, as long as the total is 500 g.

500 g self-raising flour
5 ml (1 tsp) salt
5 ml (1 tsp) baking powder
250 ml (1 cup) sugar
500 ml (2 cups) porridge oats
75 ml (5 Tbsp) currants (optional)
125 g butter, melted
2 large free-range eggs
about 250 ml (1 cup) buttermilk
90 ml (6 Tbsp) oil

Sift the flour, salt and baking powder into a large bowl. If using bran-rich flour, add the bran left in the sieve. Mix in the sugar, oats and currants, if using, then mix in the melted butter. In a separate bowl, whisk the eggs, buttermilk and oil, then add to the flour mixture. Combine well; the dough should be squishy and soft. If using a lot of bran-rich flour, you will need a little extra buttermilk. Turn the dough into either a 26 x 9 x 7 cm loaf tin, oiled and then lined (base and sides) with baking paper, or a 20 x 26 cm baking tin, lined in the same way. In both cases, spread evenly, levelling the top with your dampened hand and a wet wooden spoon. Bake the rectangular batch at 180 °C for 45 minutes. The loaf tin, being deeper, will take about 1 hour. Cool before turning out. For perfect finger shapes, cut off the crusty sides before cutting across into thick slices and then into fingers. Arrange on baking sheets lined with several layers of baking paper (as the rusks tend to brown quickly) and dry out in a very low oven, about 100 °C, for several hours, turning once. Once dry, leave to cool in the oven before storing. Makes dozens, depending on how thick and short or long and thinly you slice the fingers.

Betsie's Blitz Coffee Cake

Betsie would have started this in a bit of a panic when she first spied the ladies through the kitchen window driving up the dusty farm road. By the time they had unlatched the three farm gates, driven through, carefully closed them again (so that the sheep wouldn't wander), and finally parked under the pepper tree in the yard, it would be in the oven. And by the time they had thoroughly inspected the rose garden, the new foal, the shearing shed and the nesting hens, it would be baked. And then by the time they had gathered round the dining-room table, gossiped a bit, and started wanting tea, it would be ready – filled with mocha butter icing, or whipped farm cream.

3 XL free-range eggs, separated
250 ml (1 cup) castor sugar
125 ml (½ cup) sunflower or canola oil
125 ml (½ cup) milk
20 ml (4 tsp) instant coffee granules, dissolved in 45 ml (3 Tbsp) lukewarm water
500 ml (2 cups) cake flour
15 ml (1 Tbsp) baking powder
a large pinch of sea salt
a pinch of cream of tartar
5 ml (1 tsp) vanilla essence
sweetened whipped cream flavoured with coffee, or mocha butter icing using 750 ml (3 cups) icing sugar

* Fold in 50 g chopped pecans at this point – optional, but special.

Using an electric whisk, whisk together the egg yolks, castor sugar, oil, milk and dissolved coffee granules. When the sugar has completely dissolved, sift the flour, baking powder and salt right in, and whisk at high speed for exactly 1 minute. Whisk the egg whites until stiff (either do this first, or use clean beaters). Add the cream of tartar and whisk again until stiff and voluminous. Using a metal spoon, fold the egg white mixture into the batter, along with the vanilla essence*. Pour into two 19 cm layer cake pans, lightly oiled and bases lined with baking paper; tilt pans gently to spread evenly. Bake on the middle shelf of the oven at 180 °C for 30 minutes until risen, pale brown and firm. Leave to stand for a few minutes, then turn out onto a rack to cool before sandwiching the layers with filling, and covering the top.

VIRGINIA

'Virginia my dear, I think we've arrived,' the Colonel said as they stepped out of their car and walked to the front gate of Number Four, a large, bow-fronted Victorian house with a **FOR SALE** sign nailed to the post-box. The gate creaked loudly as they pushed it open and Lily hurried over from the house opposite.

'Yoo-hoo! I was just having tea on my stoep when I happened to see you.' She put out her hand. 'I'm Lily from over the way.'

'Blake-Sampson,' said the Colonel. 'My wife, Virginia.'

Lily pumped their hands. 'I'm *so* pleased to meet you. Are you buyers? I *do* hope so. The place has been empty for ages. You'll probably get it for a song. Come.'

Without waiting for a reply, Lily ushered them along the pavement. 'I'll take you straight to Daleen. She's the agent you know, and her office is right over there above the Corner Shop.'

'Well, my dear,' the Colonel remarked to Virginia later that day as they sat in the lounge of the Corriebush Boarding House, sipping gin and tonic, 'that was a piece of cake, wasn't it? Talk about a song! I'd call it a gift.'

'Precisely what we wanted, William, and it just fell into our laps. I can't wait to move in so that you can get started. When do you think the furniture will arrive?'

'Should be here the day after tomorrow. Port Elizabeth isn't far away after all.'

'It's coming in one of those big vans,' Lily told Herman, her husband.

'Been sitting there in storage ever since they arrived. Came with them on the ship from London. They're English, you know.'

'How do you know this?' he asked

'Because they told me, that's how. I called on them this morning.'

'So soon already?'

Lily gave a pained sigh. '*Ag,* Herman. When a person's sitting in a boarding house in a strange town, a friendly face is a welcome sight.'

'Not sticking your nose into their business, are you?'

Lily ignored him. 'They'll be moving in tomorrow, and I'll be lending a a hand.'

Herman sniffed. 'And asking a lot of questions no doubt.'

'Not a lot, just one thing really, because we're neighbours after all. I'd like to know what they're doing here. That's reasonable, isn't it?'

'That's reasonable, but don't ask it straight. Don't say: "What are you doing here?" Let them rather tell you. It's more polite that way.'

Lily gave nothing away when she returned from her day of helping.

'*Sjoe!* The dust!' she exclaimed and went off to have a bath. Herman waited. Powdered and changed, she went to the kitchen to make the supper. He put his head round the door. She was peeling potatoes.

'Lovely fresh ones,' she remarked. 'I think they're Van der Planks.'

Some time later, Lily tinkled the bell, Herman came in from the stoep, and they sat down to eat. Still she said nothing.

'Dammit Lily. What are they doing here?'

'Herman, you should have seen the furniture! Grand isn't the word. Even a piano, never mind all the silver and pictures and stuff. And the books! Never seen so many books outside a library.'

'So what are they doing here, Lily?'

'They even brought a cat basket.'

'LILY!'

'Salt and pepper?' she asked, and when Herman did not reply, she put down her knife and fork, dabbed her lips with a napkin, shooed the dog from under her feet and took several sips of water.

'You are going to be very, very surprised.'

Herman raised an eyebrow, but carried on eating. 'Well, don't you want to hear?' she asked.

'*Ja*, I'm waiting. Get on with it now, old woman.'

'Just let me fill the kettle.'

'*Ag,* come on Lily, enough is enough.'

' Well then, as you know I'm never one to beat about the bush, so I'll tell you straight. The Colonel is writing a book.'

'He's come to Corriebush to write a book?'

'He's come here to write a book.'

'What's wrong with England, then?'

'Nothing wrong with England.'

'Then why does he come to write a book in Corriebush with all his stuff?'

Lily shrugged. 'You said I mustn't ask a lot of questions, so I didn't,' she replied smugly. 'So that's all I know. For the present.'

William Rupert Blake-Sampson was just eighteen years old when the Anglo-Boer War broke out. His application to read English at Oxford had just been approved, but his father had been a Colonel in the army in India, and William and his older brother would never have missed a chance to fight for the glory of the Empire. They signed up right away, confident that the war would be over in a matter of months, maybe even weeks. A handful of Boer farmers would hardly be a match for the English army. William felt supremely confident and invulnerable, standing on the deck of the troopship as it left Southampton on a bleak December day in 1899. Several thousand voices sang lustily as the ship slipped its moorings and headed into the Channel. 'Wish me luck as you wave me goodbye…'

Shortly after his arrival at the Cape, William was posted as a mounted infantryman – one of about 100 000 men under Lord Roberts' command, who set out on a march from Bloemfontein to their target up north – Pretoria. William did not get far. Just six days later, in the veld beyond Smaldeel, his horse went lame. He dismounted, and discovered a gash on the horse's right back leg, probably caused by shrapnel when they had come under fire the previous day. It was a shallow wound, but already it was infected, with green flies clustering around and burrowing into the flesh. The men closest to William had stopped when he did, but he'd waved them on, saying he would clean it up as quickly as he could and follow on slowly. He should never have stopped, and they should never have ridden on. In this war, in this country, the enemy fought from the hills, appeared from behind kopjes, sheltered in kloofs and valleys, and could ambush a whole regiment by hiding in a donga, or ditch. The terrain was totally unfamiliar to the British, but it was home to these Boer men of the veld and they used it to brilliant advantage.

William spoke soothingly to his horse while he used his pocket knife to remove as much of the shrapnel as he could. It was when he was about to disinfect the wound that he began to feel giddy. It was the month of May, but the cruel summer heat had not yet given way to autumn's cooler weather. The humidity was unbearable, the veld bleached to a lifeless, dust-choked desert. Sweat poured down his face, his neck, his back, down his legs in their baggy breeches and into his boots, and above him the sky began to spin in pale, dizzying circles. He felt his way to a rock, sank down and reached for his water bottle.

The rifle was pushed in between his shoulder blades with such force that William's head snapped backwards.

'Stand up Tommy, and don't turn round. Put up your hands and don't move or I might just miss the fatal spot, and then you'll die here slowly, lying in the dust like a helpless, grovelling worm.'

For one insane moment William thought of ducking and turning and fighting the Boer with his fists, but his body was shaking uncontrollably. He could not even lift his arms. His tongue was thick and his voice was a strangled gasp. 'Shoot,' he heard himself saying. 'Just shoot and get it done.'

'Don't be in such a hurry man,' the voice behind him said. 'Suffer first. Perhaps you were the one who burnt down my father's house? Set fire to everything we owned, even our sheepdogs? Or were you one of those who stood and smiled as my mother and sisters were carted off in a wagon to the concentration camp? Tell me Tommy, was it you?

Were you one of those bastards? Take your time, Tommy, take your time before you answer. I can wait, while I decide on the best punishment for a scavenging coward.'

William stood, still trembling, vaguely aware of the red ants swarming around his boots in the livid, hot red dust. And then suddenly his fear turned to rage, and he heard himself shouting defiantly.

'I saw four of my friends shot to pieces by you Boers!' he shouted. 'Shot and bleeding and left to die while you ran back to your hills to hide!'

His anger made him reckless and he started to turn round, but the rifle bit deeper into his back.

'Bloody fool,' the man said. 'Tell me how old are you Tommy? I'm standing right behind you and I see there's still a bit of green behind your ears.'

William remained silent.

'Tommy, HOW OLD ARE YOU?'

'Eighteen.'

'Child. Poor, ridiculous child fighting a war you cannot win. Why don't you go home to your mother? Eighteen years old and already a thief and a bastard. Poor, ridiculous child.'

Suddenly the aching thrust of the rifle ceased. A hand gripped William's shoulder and spun him round.

Facing him was a young, powerfully built Boer, with thick black eyebrows and a dark beard, not yet fully grown. They stood there, the two soldiers, and looked at each other for an eternity, blue eyes staring straight into brown, both unwavering. And then the Boer put out his hand.

'Gideon Loots,' he said. 'Now give me your water bottle, your rifle and your bandolier. Your boots too. Take your lame animal, it's no good to me. But I'll have that stupid helmet of yours, I'll turn it over and use it to water my horse. Why don't you wear a real man's hat like we do? And now *voetsek!* Go! And run before I change my mind. If you go up that road you'll find your foolish comrades somewhere near Welgelegen.'

Lily repeated the whole story to Herman, exactly as she had heard it from Virginia.

'And now the Colonel has come to find Gideon Loots. All his life he has remembered this man, and he wants to shake him by the hand and thank him. And now that he's retired, he wants to write books about his military experiences, and especially the one about Gideon, and the war.'

'But why must he write it in Corriebush?'

'Because it's small and quiet and far away from the battlefields, so he will be able to think fairly and clearly. That's what Virginia says. Also, he thinks Gideon Loots might have come from these parts. He's done some enquiring.'

'But Lily, that war was a terrible thing. They were our enemies, remember, and now they want to come and live with us?'

'Now you're being really stupid, Herman. What's past is past, I say. Every nation makes terrible mistakes. One doesn't forget, but one has to forgive. Forgive, and you will be forgiven. It's the way of the world, and if it isn't it should be.'

'You're always right, old woman.'

'Yes I am. And all of us are going to make them as happy as can be, especially Virginia. She's rather quiet, a private sort if you know what I mean, and she could get a bit lonely with him being busy at his desk all day. The Colonel told me he thought if they brought some of their furniture she might settle down more easily.'

'Hmmph. Not much for the poor lady to do in Corriebush.'

'Nonsense. We've already planned a welcome picnic by the river. You can't come, it's for women only, so we can really let our hair down.'

Nellie and Maria, Sophia and Anna, Amelia and Lily all contributed to a giant picnic hamper. The day was soft and sunny and they had just settled onto the rugs and started on the chicken when Virginia drank half a bottle of wine.

The group stared in astonishment, especially Sophia, who prided herself on never touching a drop.

'Not since the day I fell out of the plum tree and my mother gave me brandy to steady my nerves and it made me so tight I took a knife and chopped off a fowl's head.'

Sophia told the story whenever there was liquor around, but this time she just sat and watched, horrified, as Virginia tossed back three glasses of wine in a few gulps. After which she started talking.

'She totally ignored my chippolatas,' Lily told Herman later, 'but, poor woman, she had to get it all out, because underneath the silk blouses and shoes from Italy, she's really a very shy and lonely person.'

'So the wine loosened her tongue.'

'Loosened her tongue, and helped her tell us everything. She sat there on the rug, drained the last drop in her glass, hugged her knees and off she went. Like this.'

'It's the Colonel,' Virginia began.

The women started to fidget with embarrassment, afraid of what they might be going to hear.

'No no, it's not what you think,' Virginia went on hurriedly. 'I adore my William. He's the kindest, most loving gentleman on earth. The trouble is he fell in love with a Red Cross nurse, coming home on a ship. You know how things are on a ship.'

They nodded.

'We know how it is on a ship.'

'And especially after a war, when people have been fighting and frightened and desperately missing their families, they tend to fall in love very quickly. But William says he found out she was engaged to a man in St Ives, and so he quickly ended the relationship.'

'Then he married you?'

'Well, not right away, but you could say he was looking to settle down. We met in London. I was helping out in a soup kitchen, and one day there he was, so handsome and charming and brave, and you could say it was love at first sight.'

'Over the soup?' asked Maria.

'Over the soup. He said he liked my youthful freshness and that I was exactly the charming, bonny girl he could see in his solemn old home.'

'Well, let me tell you, that solemn old home is a very large and grand place on the Blake-Sampson estate, Erin Park, and I – well, I had grown up in a small village in Yorkshire and

Erin Park really took me by surprise. Suddenly I was mistress of a huge estate and there was so much I had to learn. William was terribly kind of course. He tried to teach me to shoot grouse, but it upset me too much, shooting those lovely birds. He tried to teach me to play bridge, but I kept trumping my partner's ace. As you know, that's something you must never do.'

'No. You must never trump your partner's ace,' they agreed.

He did not like me to work in the garden. He said that was the groundsman's job. And he didn't like to see me in the kitchen, either, even though I'm a good cook; learnt at my mother's knee, as they say. But he said that's what he employed two cooks for. And then there were all those house parties. We entertained often. He said I looked so beautiful in the clothes and jewellery he had bought me and he loved watching me chatting to his guests over our candle-lit dinners. For a while this was fine, he was such a caring husband, but then I began to feel just useless.'

'Babies?' Amelia asked.

'Old war injury,' Virginia explained, and they nodded understandingly.

'When he went away to the First World War I thought I would die. But after a while I learnt I could have fun in the kitchen – I did learn a lot from my mother, as I said, and William's cooks taught me a great deal more, especially the one from France. But when he came back from the war, all full of medals, he once again wanted me by his side all the time. He really loves me you know, but I long to do something to make him really proud of me so that people don't always speak of me as the Colonel's sweet but rather useless little wife. And now here in Corriebush, I see no chance of that. Nothing to do. I just don't know how I'm going to last until he finishes this book.' Virginia started to cry. 'And now I've gone and hurt all you kind, sweet ladies and I feel awful and I'm so sorry. Nellie, have you a pill? My head is starting to ache.'

'Have something to eat, it will help,' said Maria, offering her a buttered bun.

On the whole, the picnic had been a success because Virginia had got a big weight off her chest, they all felt closer, and lending a helping hand was really what the Corriebush women liked best.

'But we have to bring back some confidence there,' said Anna, when they were discussing the whole business the following day.

'Give her a chance to show off her talents.'

'But she said she was useless.'

'But she also said she liked to cook.'

'And there's the Annual Baking Competition coming up soon. This year the theme is Chocolate Cake.'

'I know, I know!' Nellie was beside herself with excitement.

'We'll give her our favourite recipes – yours and mine and everyone else's, they're all a little bit different – and encourage her to enter. And then…'

She needed explain no further. Already six pairs of eyes were beginning to sparkle.

During the week of the competition, the very air in Corriebush was thick with the aroma of baking: chocolate and cocoa, butter and vanilla, and sponges rising in ovens all over the town, while the constant clatter of spoons and tins and whisks tinkled out from every kitchen.

'Sounds as if a whole flock of guineafowl has come to town,' Herman remarked.

On the morning of the big day, they all gathered at Amelia's house with their bounteous, beautiful chocolate cakes.

'Bless my soul, Maria, you've really done it this time!'

'Too good to eat, Anna!'

'Nellie, yours simply takes the cake. I've never seen such a smelter of icing.'

'You mean welter, Sophia.'

'Smelter, welter, what's the difference? It's a beauty!'

'Poor Virginia, she wouldn't have stood a chance if we hadn't thought of *our plan*.'

And gleefully they put it into action. First they lovingly set their cakes out on Amelia's large kitchen table and then carried out the operation, one by one. A deep breath, and there they went, without a single shudder or flinch. First Anna turned her back on her offering, and sat on it. Then Maria carefully positioned six dead flies among her beautiful little chocolate rosettes. Lily threw a cup of tea over hers. Sophia picked hers up and dropped it on the floor. Nellie cut a slice out of hers and ate it. Amelia burst into tears and left her crumpled handkerchief pressed deeply into the top. Then they took them to the hall.

'Whatever Virginia has come up with, it will definitely be better than this lot,' they all agreed, as they marched up the steps.

Virginia arrived soon after. Shyly she placed her cake at one end of the table. Maria nudged Lily, who nudged Sophia, who nudged Anna, who was already tugging at the others. They were knocked speechless.

Virginia had made a chocolate truffle gâteau. Four layers of chocolate sponge, sandwiched with chocolate melted with double cream; over the top she had poured a layer of rich glacé icing; and on this she had spelt out the name CORRIEBUSH with miniature rum truffles and maraschino cherries. The whole glorious affair sat poised on a crystal cake stand, surrounded by candied violets.

'A work of art!' the judges exclaimed.

'A work of art!' the women repeated, shaking their heads in disbelief.

Virginia blushed with embarrassment. 'To me it looks rather like a Caribbean sunhat.'

'That too,' they nodded.

'The recipe comes from a French book,' Virginia explained, feeling really awkward now that she had seen their cakes at the other end of the table. 'I just dolled it up a bit.'

When the judges placed the red card reading First Prize in front of Virginia's cake, all the women clapped, and Amelia told her she was a dark horse and that she should take it home quickly, before they all started nibbling, and share it with the Colonel for tea.

The rest of them carried their cakes home, quite happily. For several blocks, however, no one spoke. Then Anna broke the silence.

'Needn't have sat on mine.'

'Put flies on mine.'

'Thrown tea over mine.'

'Dropped mine.'

'Eaten half mine.'

'Never seen a cake like that. I wish she would show us how.'

'That's it! That's it! Yoo-hoo!' Anna called to Virginia, who was trying to push open the gate to Number Four with her knee, while carefully balancing her cake in both hands. 'Listen, we've got a lovely plan.'

They wasted no time in getting it off the ground.

Every Monday morning for the following three months, they all gathered in Maria's big kitchen, while Virginia led them through some English Country Cooking.

'She's showing us a thing or two about fancy foreign food,' Anna told Herman, proudly setting a perfectly roasted sirloin of beef before him, with Yorkshire pudding, crisp and puffed up and golden brown on the side.

Virginia followed up with English Rhubarb Crumble, Bubble and Squeak and Wiltshire Tatties, then continued with slightly more sophisticated recipes like English Cider Cake and Fig Pudding with Brandy Butter, which of course Sophia wouldn't touch because of the brandy.

Every Wednesday morning it was the Corriebush ladies' turn, when Virginia learnt all about koeksisters and sosaties, tomato bredie, pumpkin fritters, watermelon preserve, apricot chutney, mealie bread, even boerewors and biltong. At the end of the lessons all the note-books were bulging with recipes, tips and new ideas.

The final class was a happy celebration, with sparkling wine and butternut soup, roast turkey and *soetpatats*, trifle and malva pudding. After which, they all rose to show each other how much weight they had gained.

'Just watch when I pinch here, under my belt. See how thick?'

'It's my backside that's got it.'

'When I nod, my neck looks just like a turkey's dangle.'

'Crop, Sophia, you mean crop.'

'Crop.'

All the husbands were delighted with the new menus and the Colonel was as pleased as punch. He had never seen Virginia so happy, and he had finished his book, although he had not managed to get news of Gideon Loots.

'We'll just have to come back again,' Virginia remarked, as the **TO RENT** sign was nailed to the front gate. 'I think we should leave some of our furniture here, then we'll feel quite at home when we return.'

'Jolly good idea, old girl,' William agreed. 'Perhaps for a few months next summer. But now I must get to my publisher, he's waiting for this manuscript and I've already drafted my next one. Got some good ideas. And in any case it will be nice to be back at Erin Park for a while.'

'Yes. Yes it will,' Virginia replied. 'I'm looking forward to it because I'm going to be very busy. I have a plan.'

William raised an eyebrow.

'I'm going to start a cookery school in Chipping Hampton!'

'Good gracious, Ginny, you are full of surprises!'

'And that's not all. When we return to Corriebush you can write your next book and I'm going to write mine. A cookery book!'

'Bingo old girl!' exclaimed the Colonel.

'Bingo William!'

Virginia waved and waved through the passenger window as her husband slid behind the wheel.

'She's a changed woman,' remarked Lily. 'Happy as a lark.'

'Found her feet in Corriebush, that's for sure!'

'And didn't she have the time of her life with those cookery lessons!'

'Simply fell into the idea like a croûton into soup.'

'I'm really so sad to see her go, even though they have promised to come back.'

'Oh my hat, my *blerrie* hat!'

'What now, Sophia?'

'We forgot to buy her a farewell present! How *could* we? After all she's taught us!'

'Don't worry ladies,' Anna reassured them. 'I've got something that will keep her smiling all the way to Port Elizabeth.'

And she slid a steaming Cornish Pasty through the window.

Virginia laughed delightedly. 'Right size, right shape, good pastry, smells gorgeous. Ten out of ten Anna!'

The Colonel accelerated, and they were gone.

VIRGINIA'S RECIPES

Due to the variety of culinary influences in her life, Virginia was a trifle confused as to where her tastes and talents lay. She was perfectly confident cooking traditional English food, of course, but then there was William's father who came home from his years in India with a great fondness for spices and kept dropping hints whenever he came to visit.

He would dab at his moustache at the end of a meal and say 'Very good, my dear, but do you know, over in the East they would have given this a bit of a lift. Not too hot, the children won't like it, but just a nip of this and that. Try it next time.'

And so she did.

And then there were the two chefs at Erin Park – one French, and the other a Yorkshireman. Goodness knows how they kept the peace in the kitchen, but they seemed to fuse quite well, and because they often invited Virginia to watch while they were working, they had a profound influence on her culinary knowledge. As a result, Virginia found it quite difficult to single out any one cuisine in her classes, and in the end she simply went for a delicious, eclectic mix.

Chilled Beetroot Soup with Avocado Cream

Imagine a bowl of incredibly vivid, magenta-coloured soup,
floated with avocado and swirled with cream, and you've got this colourful wonder.
It's the sort of soup photographers love to shoot, set out in white bowls on a table on a patio.
Blue sky, bougainvillea, beautiful people, beetroot soup. It's a fun soup, and easy as pie
to make because the ingredients are so basic.

15 ml (1 Tbsp) each oil and butter
1 medium onion, sliced into thin rings
2 large leeks, white parts only,
well washed and chopped
15 ml (1 Tbsp) water
450–500 g potatoes,
peeled and cubed
2 ml (½ tsp) each grated nutmeg
and paprika
1 litre (4 cups) hot chicken stock
2 bay leaves
a little sea salt
a good pinch of sugar
2 medium, raw beetroot,
peeled and coarsely grated
(about 230 g peeled weight)
125 ml (½ cup) milk
a little fresh lemon juice
white vermouth (optional)
cubed or balled avocado, and softly
whipped cream (or thick sour cream
or creamy Greek yoghurt), and milled
black pepper – these are not just
garnishes, they are essentials

Heat the oil and butter in a really large saucepan (because grated beetroot is bulky), and add the onion and leeks. Toss until coated, then add the water and sweat, covered, over very low heat until soft and golden; do not brown. Add the potatoes, nutmeg and paprika, toss to mix, then add the stock, bay leaves, seasoning and beetroot. Cover and simmer very gently until the vegetables are cooked – about 25 minutes. Remove from heat, stir in the milk and, when reasonably cool, whizz in a blender, in batches, until smooth. Check the seasoning – if it needs a little oomph, shake in a few drops of lemon juice. Refrigerate. To serve, ladle into the soup bowls. If using vermouth, it goes in before the garnish – just a dash. Spoon a large dollop of cream on top, gently mix in a generous helping of the cubed or balled avocado, then grind over a little black pepper. **Serves 6–8.**

CAULIFLOWER VICHYSSOISE WITH NUTMEG AND LEMON

This is a slightly different version of the classic creamy potato and leek soup,
offering a new taste without altogether changing the character of the original,
and a good choice when you need a soup that's unfailingly popular, quick to make,
and doesn't require a shopping trip because the ingredients are already in your pantry.
Although vichyssoise is traditionally served cold, chilling does tend to dull the flavour,
and this one is best served hot.

30 ml (2 Tbsp) each oil and butter
2 medium onions, chopped
4 large leeks, white parts only, chopped
700 g potatoes, peeled and cubed
500 g cauliflower florets
7 ml (1½ tsp) grated nutmeg
4 x 4 cm strips lemon peel
2 litres (8 cups) hot chicken stock
4 bay leaves
sea salt to taste
125 ml (½ cup) each milk and thick cream
lemon juice (optional)
snipped chives to garnish

Heat the oil and butter in a large saucepan, add the onions and leeks and sweat over low heat, shaking the pan occasionally and taking care that the vegetables do not brown. When soft and pale, add the potatoes, cauliflower and nutmeg and toss to mix, then add the remaining ingredients except the milk and cream. Cover and simmer until the vegetables are soft, about 25 minutes. Leave to cool down a bit, remove the bay leaves and lemon peel, then purée in a blender, in batches, until smooth. Return to the saucepan, add the milk and cream and reheat, stirring, without boiling. Check seasoning – the soup might need a little more salt, and a squeeze of lemon juice to sharpen the flavour. Ladle into warmed soup bowls and sprinkle with chives. **Serves 8–10.**

Cucumber and Avocado Soup on Ice

This is a thick and gorgeous soup, so smooth and rich that it needs no extras,
not even a cobweb of cream. The garnish, so to speak, comes in the form of little
dill fronds frozen in ice cubes. It's altogether a smashing combination,
amazingly easy to make and the fresh, funky colour is stunning.

1 x 550–600 g English cucumber
(that's a *big* one)
15 ml (1 Tbsp) each oil and butter
2 medium leeks, chopped
1 medium onion, chopped
500 ml (2 cups) hot chicken stock
a small clutch of parsley tufts
2 bay leaves
a little sea salt
2 medium or 1 jumbo avocado, diced
(300 g flesh, once peeled and pipped)
2–3 small fronds of fresh dill
15 ml (1 Tbsp) fresh lime juice
finely grated rind of ½ small lime

Pare the cucumber, cut in half and remove the seeds, then dice. Heat the oil and butter in a deep saucepan, add the leeks and onion and cook slowly until soft and transparent. Mix in the cucumber and cook briefly until it has started to shrink a little. Add the stock, parsley, bay leaves and salt, then cover and simmer for about 25 minutes until the vegetables are very soft. Leave to cool, then remove the bay leaves, add the avocado flesh, the dill, lime juice and rind, and whizz in a blender until beautifully thick and smooth. Pour into a large glass jug, drop in the avocado pip, then cover and refrigerate for at least 6 hours, or even overnight.

During this time, make the DILLED ICE CUBES. Empty an ice cube tray and, in the hollows, place a small frond of dill, fill up with water, and freeze. Use a tray with small, round hollows or, if yours makes large cubes, only half-fill them with water, otherwise the cubes will take too long to melt. Check the seasoning, give the soup a good stir, remove the avo pip and pour into small bowls (not soup plates). Drop two dilly ice cubes into each bowl, then go away for a few minutes to allow them to just start melting before serving.
Serves 6–8.

Fish with Lime-Chive Butter and Glazed Mushrooms

Kabeljou (kob), with its firm, succulent flesh, is the perfect choice for this recipe.
Fish often responds best when fiddled with least, and this is a fine example
of just how good it can be when given the easy, no-fuss treatment.
The mushrooms make a fabulous (also dead easy) accompaniment.

1 smallish lime
60 g soft butter
30 ml (2 Tbsp) finely snipped chives
a dash of Pernod (optional)
4 large, skinless fish fillets, preferably
kabeljou (about 700 g)
oil and sea salt

Start by making the butter. Use a zester or a coarse grater for the lime, and then chop the peel finely, or snip with a pair of kitchen scissors. Reserve the shaved lime to use for juice later on. Mix the peel with the butter, chives and Pernod, if using. Roll into a long sausage, wrap in greaseproof paper and refrigerate until firm.

Shortly before you want to eat, line a shallow baking dish with greaseproof paper and brush with oil. Place the fish fillets on the paper, brush the tops very lightly with oil, sprinkle with salt and drizzle with lime juice. Bake at 180 °C until cooked through – the time depends on the thickness of the fish – probably 25 minutes. While the fish is baking, slice the butter into coins and, just before serving, place one or two coins on top of each fillet. Return to the oven until they just start to melt and spread, then serve, using a spatula to lift out onto serving plates. **Serves 4.**

Glazed mushrooms

These little nuggets can be prepared in advance, spooned into a baking dish, and reheated in the oven shortly before the fish is done.

250 g white mushrooms
45 ml (3 Tbsp) medium-sweet sherry
45 ml (3 Tbsp) chicken stock
15 ml (1 Tbsp) soy sauce
10 ml (2 tsp) tomato paste
5 ml (1 tsp) treacle sugar
a little chopped parsley

Wipe the mushrooms with damp kitchen paper and, if the mushrooms are large, slice into halves or quarters. Place in a wide-based frying pan in a single layer as far as possible. Mix the sherry, stock, soy sauce and tomato paste together and pour over the mushrooms, then sprinkle with the sugar. Bring to the boil and cook over high heat, tossing and stirring. The mushrooms will release a lot of liquid at first, but as the liquid reduces they will start to sizzle in their own juices – watch for burning. Remove from the heat as soon as the liquid evaporates into caramelly bubbles. Spoon into a shallow baking dish, rinse out the frying pan with just a dash of water, drizzle over the mushrooms to keep them moist, sprinkle with parsley and reheat briefly, as suggested above.

CHILLED SMOKED SALMON PATTIES WITH DILLY MAYO AND WALNUT BREAD

These make the most elegant and enticing starters: plump little patties,
a drizzle of light mayonnaise, and crunchy brown walnut bread speckled with red pepper.
Not too rich, not too expensive (the salmon is padded out with other things),
not at all tricky to make, and everything tied up in advance – you can even make
them a day ahead and refrigerate overnight. Present prettily on small plates.

160 g smoked salmon, finely snipped
(off-cuts are fine to use)
1 hard-boiled free-range egg, chopped
4 slim spring onions, chopped
30 ml (2 Tbsp) finely chopped parsley
5 ml (1 tsp) capers,
rinsed and chopped
5 ml (1 tsp) Dijon mustard
10 ml (2 tsp) lime juice (or lemon,
but use a little less)
200 g smooth, fat-free cottage cheese
milled black pepper and a little sea
salt and sugar to taste

DILLY MAYO
30 ml (2 Tbsp) mayonnaise,
preferably home-made
30 ml (2 Tbsp) thick, plain yoghurt
10 ml (2 tsp) chopped fresh dill
2 ml (½ tsp) Dijon mustard
a small trickle of honey

For the salmon patties, mix everything together. To mould, you will need 4 to 6 small ramekins – flattish and shallow – 6 cm in diameter and 3 cm deep is just right. Four ramekins will give you really generous patties; six will provide small appetite-whetters – the better option if a good dinner is to follow. Line each with clingfilm, with enough overhang to cover the tops. Divide the mixture between the ramekins, pressing in gently to make a flat cake. Cover with the overhanging clingfilm and refrigerate for several hours or overnight. When needed, simply lift out of the ramekin, remove the clingfilm and out should plop a perfect patty.

For the mayonnaise, stir everything together until mixed, then cover and refrigerate.
Makes just enough to spoon alongside 6 patties.
Serves 4–6.

Walnut and red pepper batter bread

A savoury, wholesome quick-mix bread, perfect with the patties.
Serve lightly buttered, sliced into fingers.

500 ml (2 cups) white bread flour
500 ml (2 cups) wholewheat flour
7 ml (1½ tsp) sea salt
15 ml (1 Tbsp) instant dry yeast
(not quite a 10 g sachet)
1 small red pepper, finely diced
a little chopped parsley for colour
15 ml (1 Tbsp) light brown sugar
50–60 g walnuts, chopped
15 ml (1 Tbsp) soft butter
about 500 ml (2 cups) very warm
(but not *hot*) water

Mix together the flours, salt, yeast, red pepper, parsley, sugar and walnuts. Stir the butter into 250 ml (1 cup) very warm water and, when melted, mix into the dry ingredients. Slowly add the remaining water (or just enough) to make a soft, sticky batter. Turn into a 26 x 9 x 7 cm loaf tin, first oiling the base and sides and then lining with baking paper. Cover lightly, and leave to rise in a warm place until the batter reaches the top of the tin – 45 minutes to 1 hour, depending on room temperature. Bake at 200 °C for 30 minutes, then at 180 °C for a further 20–30 minutes until firm and brown. Stand for 5 minutes before turning out onto a rack, remove baking paper, and leave to cool.

Spicy Indian-style Butter Chicken

This dish really does taste as good as it looks: tender nuggets of chicken
in a smooth red sauce, fresh green coriander and saffron-tinted basmati rice –
the colour combination is brilliant. Skinless thigh fillets are just perfect here – they're not
bulky or greasy and, unlike breast fillets, they won't dry out despite the long, slow simmer.
This dish may be made a day ahead and chilled overnight in a suitable container.

2 x 410 g cans Indian Diced Tomatoes
(with curry leaves and spices)
45 ml (3 Tbsp) oil
1.2 kg skinless chicken thigh fillets
60 ml (4 Tbsp) butter
10 ml (2 tsp) each ground cumin,
curry powder and paprika
5 ml (1 tsp) ground cinnamon
about 20 ml (4 tsp) finely chopped,
peeled root ginger
a pinch of crushed dried chillies
(optional)
about 10 ml (2 tsp) sea salt
15 ml (1 Tbsp) sugar
a little fresh lemon juice, if necessary
90 ml (6 Tbsp) thick, plain yoghurt
10 ml (2 tsp) garam masala and
a handful of fresh coriander
leaves to garnish

Empty the cans of tomatoes into a blender and whizz until smooth, then set aside. Heat the oil in a wide, deep saucepan. Add the chicken, toss until just sealed and pale beige on both sides, then remove and set aside. Immediately reduce the heat to very low, add the butter and, when melted, sprinkle in the ground spices and ginger. Sizzle briefly until aromatic, then return the chicken and mix in the blended tomatoes, as well as the chillies, salt and sugar. At this stage the mixture will seem too thick, but don't add any liquid, the sauce will soon thin out sufficiently. Cover and simmer very gently, stirring now and then for 50–60 minutes, or until the chicken is very tender and the sauce medium-thick and richly coloured. If the flavour needs a little lift, add a dash of lemon juice, then swirl in the yoghurt, sprinkle with the garnishes, and heat through without boiling. Ladle the chicken and sauce alongside servings of saffron basmati rice, and accompany with a bright green vegetable or salad. **Serves 6–8.**

Tarragon and Lemon Cream Chicken Breasts

Subtly flavoured and richly sauced, this is stove-top chicken at it's elegant best.
Surprisingly few ingredients are required, and the chief players –
lemon grass, honey and crème fraîche – combine quite brilliantly.

**4 skinless chicken breast fillets
(about 400 g)
15 ml (1 Tbsp) oil and a small
pat of butter
375 ml (1½ cups) chicken stock
(home-made makes a huge difference)
4–6 spring onions, chopped
5 ml (1 tsp) dried tarragon
5 ml (1 tsp) very finely grated
lemon rind
2 stalks lemon grass (whole, white,
lower stems, outer layer peeled)
15 ml (1 Tbsp) runny honey
2 ml (½ tsp) sea salt
75–90 ml (5–6 Tbsp) crème fraîche***

*** A French-style, smooth, very
rich, thick cultured cream.
If unobtainable, substitute
cultured sour cream.**

Make a few shallow slashes on the skinned side of the chicken, then flatten the breasts slightly by thumping gently with a rolling pin – be careful not to tear them. Heat the oil and butter in a large frying pan and seal the chicken on both sides; do this quickly – they must not brown at all. Remove from the pan and set aside. Lower the heat and add the stock, spring onions, tarragon (crush this with your fingers as you sprinkle it in), lemon rind, lemon grass, honey and salt to the pan. Stir to mix, then simmer, half covered, for 12–15 minutes until slightly thickened and reduced. Discard the lemon grass and stir in 75 ml (5 Tbsp) of the crème fraîche and, when smoothly combined, return the chicken to the pan. Cover and simmer very gently until the chicken is just cooked through – about 6 minutes. Now check. The sauce should be medium-thick and fairly generous, so if it reduced too much at the start, you might want to add more crème fraîche, or a little extra stock – at this stage you have to play it by ear, at the same time being careful not to mask the delicate flavour of the sauce. When you're happy, serve. Rice timbales (rice cooked in stock with bright things added, like parsley and chopped red pepper, then moulded and unmoulded) are not much trouble to make, and suit the dish well.
Serves 4.

BUCKINGHAM CHICKEN WITH LITCHIS AND ALMONDS

Everyone knows and loves Coronation Chicken. This is a new take on the theme.
It's quicker, easier and somewhat lighter, without compromising on the
splendid flavour of cold chicken in a creamy curry sauce.

4 large free-range chicken breasts
(about 900 g), with bone and skin
500 ml (2 cups) water
a few slices of onion
a few sprigs of parsley
5 ml (1 tsp) turmeric
2–3 bay leaves
a sprinkling of sea salt
1 large bunch spring onions, chopped
1 x 410 g can pitted litchis, drained,
slivered and patted dry
toasted almond flakes to garnish

DRESSING
250 ml (1 cup) low-fat
or fat-free thick, plain yoghurt
250 ml (1 cup) choice,
thick mayonnaise
45–60 ml (3–4 Tbsp) curry *paste*
(not powder) e.g. Pakco
about 5 ml (1 tsp) honey

Poach the chicken in the water with the onion, parsley, turmeric, bay leaves and salt. Cook gently, turning once and, when done, leave to cool in the stock. Remove the flesh by pulling it off with your fingers, shredding it into pieces and discarding the skin, bone and gristle. Place in a large bowl, mix in the spring onions and litchis, then slowly drizzle over about 125 ml (½ cup) of the *strained* stock. The chicken flesh will slowly absorb the stock; when it starts to run to the base of the bowl, add no more.

To make the dressing, mix the yoghurt, mayonnaise and curry paste (start with 45 ml) with the honey (even a touch of honey really rounds out the flavour, particularly if you have used fat-free yoghurt). Taste and add more curry paste if wanted, then pour two-thirds of the dressing over the chicken, tossing gently until thoroughly combined. Cover and refrigerate for a few hours, or overnight; refrigerate the extra dressing as well. To serve, spoon the chicken onto a large, flat platter, pour the extra dressing over the top (or serve it separately), and finish off with the almonds. Serve with chutney, a rice or couscous salad, and something fresh and green. **Serves 6.**

FILLET OF BEEF WITH PORT AND MUSHROOMS

This is a special occasion, rather extravagant and sensually rich dish,
with redcurrant jelly and crème fraîche adding a gourmet touch.
It's also very quick to prepare, and has to be served immediately, so have everything
ready and waiting because once you've started cooking you'll have nearly finished.

30 ml (2 Tbsp) oil
20 ml (4 tsp) butter
4 slices beef fillet of equal size and
thickness, weighing about 125 g each
sea salt and milled black pepper
6 slim spring onions, chopped
200 g brown mushrooms,
wiped and sliced
90 ml (6 Tbsp) port
300 ml (1⅛ cups) hot beef stock
7 ml (1½ tsp) Dijon mustard
10 ml (2 tsp) redcurrant jelly
45–60 ml (3–4 Tbsp) crème fraîche
(or thick sour cream)

Heat the oil and butter and, when sizzling, add the steaks. When deeply browned on one side, turn and do the other. If you don't want them rare, reduce the heat to medium and cook just until they're done to your liking, then remove, season lightly and keep warm. Add the onions, mushrooms and port to the pan juices and cook for a few minutes until almost dry, then add the stock, mustard, jelly and crème fraîche. Simmer uncovered until slightly reduced and thickened, check the seasoning, and then either nap the waiting steaks with the sauce, or serve it alongside, or make a pool on warmed plates and place the steaks on top. It might sound strange, but simple mashed potatoes are really good with this steak; alternatively, use tiny jacket potatoes, and bright vegetables. **Serves 4.**

Braised Lamb Steaks with Wine and Herbs

The 'proper' meat to use here would be stewing mutton, which requires long,
slow cooking, but there's nothing wrong with treating steaks in the same way –
they won't turn out pink, but that matters not when it comes to the taste test:
savoury, succulent lamb stew to serve with sprouts and spuds in fine British tradition.

4 lamb steaks (about 600 g)
30 ml (2 Tbsp) oil and a nut of butter
1 large onion, finely chopped
30 ml (2 Tbsp) red wine
a pinch of sugar
2 leeks, thinly sliced
4 slender carrots, diced
30 ml (2 Tbsp) flour
1 sprig of fresh rosemary and
4 sprigs of fresh thyme
125 ml (½ cup) extra red wine
250 ml (1 cup) *hot* beef stock
5 ml (1 tsp) Worcestershire sauce
2 bay leaves
a little sea salt
125 g brown mushrooms,
wiped and sliced
20 ml (4 tsp) redcurrant jelly

Carefully pull off the thin outer rind from each steak and then slice each into four. Heat the oil and butter in a large, deep saucepan (unless you have a very large, deep frying pan), and brown the lamb well on each side, then remove from the pan. Add the onion, the 30 ml (2 Tbsp) red wine and the sugar to the pan, and cook until the wine has evaporated and the onion has started to brown. Add the leeks and carrots (if there's no more fat left, add a dash of water to prevent burning). Stir for a few minutes, then return the meat to the pan, sprinkle with the flour and, when that's absorbed, add the herbs, the extra red wine, the stock, Worcestershire sauce, bay leaves and salt. Cover securely and simmer over *very* low heat for 1 hour, shaking the pan (or giving the contents a gentle stir) occasionally. After an hour the meat should be tender and the gravy thickened. Remove the bay leaves and herb stalks – the leaves will have fallen off – and add the mushrooms. Cover again and simmer for 15 minutes while they release their juices, then stir in the jelly and allow to melt. If time allows, cool the stew for a while and then reheat gently, for the finest flavour. **Makes 4 generous servings.**

Pork Chops with Cider, Apples and Sage

Cider crops up frequently in British cooking. There's cider cake, cider pears,
cider with brisket, cider with duck, cider with mussels – but in the end the marriage
that seems most natural is that of cider with pork. Add in some apples, fresh sage
and a few other bits and bobs, give it all a slow-bake, and out comes a homely
but very good casserole to serve with cabbage and mash.

15 ml (1 Tbsp) oil and a dab of butter

1 really large onion, sliced into thin rings

4 large pork leg chops (650–700 g), 2–2.5 cm thick, rind and excess fat removed

a little sea salt and ground cinnamon

30 ml (2 Tbsp) flour

125 ml (½ cup) hot, seasoned chicken stock

250 ml (1 cup) extra-dry cider

about 6 fresh sage leaves, roughly torn

10 ml (2 tsp) Dijon mustard

a few rinsed and chopped capers (optional)

15 ml (1 Tbsp) light honey

2 medium dessert apples (not Grannies), peeled and chopped

Heat the oil and butter in a wide frying pan. Add the onion and cook until just beginning to colour – adding a pinch of sugar helps. Transfer to a baking dish just big enough to take the chops in a single layer, and deep enough to hold the sauce. Spread the onions over the base. In the pan, fry the chops on both sides; keep the heat to medium (high heat toughens pork chops) and remove when they're lightly toasted in colour. Place on top of the onions and sprinkle with salt and a little cinnamon. Stir the flour into the pan drippings (if there aren't any, add a spoon of oil or butter) and, when it starts to colour, add the stock and the cider. Bring to the boil, stirring vigorously to smooth out any lumps, then remove from the heat. Add the remaining ingredients and slowly pour over the chops, tucking the diced apples wherever there's room in between. Cover the dish with greaseproof (not waxed) paper and then with foil, and bake just below the centre of the oven at 160 °C. (Bake the potatoes for the mash at the same time.) Leave the casserole alone for 1½ hours, then turn the chops. Re-cover, and bake for a further 30 minutes, or until the chops are very tender in a savoury gravy, remembering that they're thick, and have little bone to conduct the heat, so they might take longer than you would expect. **Serves 4.**

STRAWBERRY AMARETTO SYLLABUB

There was a time when, in order to make syllabub, you had to milk a cow into a bowl. There's a lot more to the story, but suffice it to say that dozens of new versions of this dessert have evolved over the years, both in and outside of England, and you no longer need a cow in order to make it. But the basics are almost always a tipple of alcohol and a lot of cream, and this version, incorporating berries and liqueur, is superb. Presentation is important, but apart from that it's one of the easiest, most luscious, do-ahead desserts imaginable.

400–450 g sweet, ripe strawberries
60 ml (¼ cup) castor sugar
60 ml (¼ cup) Amaretto liqueur
a squeeze, about 5 ml (1 tsp), fresh lemon juice
a little milled black pepper (optional)
250 ml (1 cup) thick cream
15 ml (1 Tbsp) icing sugar
toasted almond flakes for topping

Rinse, hull and dry the strawberries, then thinly slice them. Spread out in a large, shallow bowl, sprinkle with the castor sugar, liqueur and lemon juice, and cover and macerate for about 1 hour. By this time lovely juices will have been drawn. Carefully pour them off – you should have almost 125 ml (½ cup) – and set aside. Spoon the strawberries into 6 red wine glasses – use glasses (or goblets for that matter) that are roundish rather than longish. If using the pepper, give a quick twist over each nest of berries – just a little. Whip the cream lightly, adding the icing sugar as you go. Slowly drizzle in the reserved juices and whip until thickish – firmer than floppy, but not stiff. Spoon over the berries; there's heaps of cream so you'll be able to pile it high. (In fact, there's enough for another helping of berries.) Sprinkle generously with almond flakes. Place the glasses on a flat tray so that they don't fall over, and transfer to the coldest part of the fridge for the rest of the day (6–8 hours). By serving time, the cream should have just started to melt and trickle down to the berries. Eat with small spoons. **Serves 6.**

CHOCOLATE MOUSSE TRIFLE

This is neither a mousse nor a trifle, but there are elements of both in this dreamy combination of chocolate and cream softly set on a base of sliced swiss roll moistened with coffee and liqueur. It makes a special-occasion, party-sized dessert, to serve in wedges with ribbons of a fruity coulis as the perfect foil. Fresh strawberries whizzed with a touch of sugar are super, while lightly poached pears blended to a smooth purée are just as good with the chocolate-coffee flavours.

1 jam-filled chocolate swiss roll (about 450 g)
125 ml (½ cup) warm, medium-strength black coffee
20 ml (4 tsp) quality coffee liqueur, e.g. Kahlúa
200 g dark chocolate
3 XL free-range egg whites
45 ml (3 Tbsp) castor sugar
250 ml (1 cup) cream
30 ml (2 Tbsp) icing sugar
a few drops of vanilla essence
chocolate scrolls to decorate (optional)

Cut the swiss roll into 1.5 cm thick slices and squish them in to fit tightly into a large, 25 cm diameter pie dish. Mix the coffee and liqueur and drizzle over evenly. Smear a small heatproof bowl with butter, add the broken-up chocolate and place over simmering water. Don't try to melt the chocolate; the blocks should just soften completely. Cool slightly. Meanwhile, whisk the egg whites until stiff, slowly add the castor sugar and whisk to a stiff meringue. Slowly add the soft chocolate in small dollops, whisking all the time. By the time it has all been incorporated, the meringue will have deflated somewhat – this is correct. Without washing the beaters, whisk the cream, icing sugar and vanilla essence until stiff. Gently fold into the chocolate-meringue, and pour over the swiss roll base. Use a spatula to spread evenly, then immediately place in the coldest part of the refrigerator and leave to firm up, loosely covered, for 24 hours before serving. Sprinkle with chocolate scrolls, if using, slice into thin wedges and use a spatula to transfer to serving plates. Drizzle coulis alongside, and serve immediately.
Serves 10–12.

Apple and Pear Dessert Cake

This is a sweetly nostalgic pud, closely related to Eve's Pudding – the traditional,
homely, sponge-topped apple dessert – but presented here with a few twists:
pears with the apples, cinnamon and almonds in the topping. Serve warm, after supper,
with thick cream, crème fraîche or vanilla ice cream, or at room temperature,
sliced into wedges, for high tea.

500 g ripe Golden Delicious apples,
peeled and chunkily chopped*

500 g ripe Packham's pears,
peeled and chopped*

100 ml (⅖ cup) light brown sugar

seeds from 1 vanilla pod, or a few
drops of vanilla essence

30 ml (2 Tbsp) water

125 g soft butter

100 ml (⅖ cup) castor sugar

2 large free-range eggs

250 ml (1 cup) self-raising flour

a pinch of sea salt

7 ml (1½ tsp) ground cinnamon

60 ml (4 Tbsp) ground almonds

30 ml (2 Tbsp) hot water

*** Try to use these varieties, as
they provide the correct texture
and sweetness.**

Stew the apples and pears with the brown sugar
and vanilla in 30 ml (2 Tbsp) water until soft. Keep
the heat low so that the fruit will release its juices
– about 12 minutes should do if the fruit is sweet
and ripe. Spoon into a lightly buttered pie dish,
23 cm in diameter and about 5 cm deep, adding
any juices. Cream the butter and castor sugar until
pale and fluffy, then whisk in the eggs, one at a
time, adding a pinch of flour with each egg. Sift
in the flour, salt and cinnamon, and fold into the
butter mixture along with the almonds. The batter
will be thick and should now be lightened by
folding in the hot water. Don't try to spread this
over the fruit, just drop it all over, in big dollops –
it will spread during the baking. Bake at 180 °C
for 35–40 minutes until golden brown and puffed
up, with just a hole or a crack here and there with
a bit of fruit peeking through. Serve warm, rather
than hot. If serving at room temperature it will be
easy to slice into wedges, as the sponge gradually
absorbs the juices. **Serves 6–8.**

Rooibos Earl Grey Fruit Cake

This is not simply your ordinary boiled fruit cake.
The marriage between Earl Grey and nature's nectar from the mountains of the Cape
makes it just that little bit different. It's a sweet, dense, almond-topped cake which –
for a boiled cake – looks quite grand.

125 g butter, cubed
250 ml (1 cup) light brown sugar
250 ml (1 cup) water
500 g fruit cake mix
juice and grated rind
of 1 lime or ½ small lemon
5 ml (1 tsp) bicarbonate of soda
3 Importers Rooibos Earl Grey sachets
2 XL free-range eggs
5 ml (1 tsp) vanilla essence
30 ml (2 Tbsp) brandy
60 ml (¼ cup) chopped glacé cherries
250 ml (1 cup) cake flour
250 ml (1 cup) self-raising flour
1 ml (¼ tsp) sea salt
2 ml (½ tsp) each ground cinnamon,
mixed spice and grated nutmeg
whole blanched almonds for topping

* For a plumper cake, use a 20 cm
tin, and allow extra baking time.

Place the butter, sugar, water, fruit cake mix, lime juice and rind, bicarbonate of soda and tea sachets into a large, deep saucepan (because the bicarb fizzes). Bring to the boil, stirring, then simmer gently, half-covered, for 15 minutes, stirring occasionally. Remove from the stove, then use a wooden spoon to press down gently on the sachets in order to release all the flavour (being careful not to break them). Leave the mixture to cool completely. Discard the tea sachets. Whisk the eggs with the vanilla and brandy and add, with the cherries, to the cold fruit mixture. Sift the flours, salt and spices, then fold into the fruit mixture. (Use a large mixing bowl to combine everything properly.) Turn the mixture into a 22 x 6 cm cake tin*, first oiled and then lined, base and sides, with baking paper. Spread evenly, and then top with almonds, like a Dundee cake. Bake on the middle shelf of the oven at 160 °C for 1¼ hours. The cake won't rise much due to the abundance of fruit, but should be richly browned. Test with a skewer and, if done, stand for 30 minutes before turning out carefully. Remove the paper and cool, almond side up. Store in an airtight container for a day or two before cutting.

ROSA

One Friday morning, Daleen, the estate agent, received a letter out of the blue.

'Funny stamps,' remarked Harry the postman. 'Where does it come from?'

Daleen shot him a look. 'Curiosity killed the cat, and patience is a virtue. Wait.'

Squinting, she held the letter up to the light, turned it over several times, reached for a pair of scissors on her desk and carefully slit the envelope at the side.

Harry drummed his fingers on the handlebars of his bicycle while Daleen slowly scanned the contents.

'Well I never,' she finally exclaimed.

Harry looked up expectantly.

'If you want to know what it says, then stop playing piano on your thingamajig. It comes from a Mr Luigi Castello, and he wants to know if there is a shop for sale in Corriebush.'

Harry pedalled off to tell the world, and Daleen immediately sent off a telegram.

'The fish shop next to Hannah's Hairdressing Salon is standing empty. Superior accommodation, with four rooms above the shop, a garden with fruit trees, a fish-fryer, chip basket, and a beautiful painted whale on the wall. A snip. Several buyers interested. Awaiting prompt reply.'

Then she sat, holding thumbs.

'I haven't sold anything in months,' she confided to Anna who, having heard the news from Harry, dropped in right away. 'Maybe an old fish shop is not everyone's cup of tea, but you never know with people. What's sauce for the goose is meat for the gander, and I really must have a sale before Christmas or its tickets.'

'I wonder how he heard about Corriebush?' Anna mused.

'Search me. Probably stuck a pin into a map of Africa.'

Mr and Mrs Castello arrived in a large van, with their family of five small sons, an older daughter and Mr Castello's aged mother, and even while they were still unloading, the news was being passed from house to house.

'I see the Italians have come to town,' Anna told Lily.

'Straight out of Rome, I hear. Coming to look for a better life in South Africa with a bit of space to raise the family. They say Rome is really full up these days.'

'He'll have a better chance to make a living out here, what with all those mouths to feed.'

'We must do our best to make them feel at home, even if we can't speak the language. I only know *arrivederci* from the song.'

As was their custom, the women wasted no time in paying a call, all six of them together, in case they needed help with translating.

'You should have heard the opera when they found us on their doorstep!' Sophia told Dawid later. 'Mr and Mrs, the six children, even the old grandmother came out all talking at the same time, and when we gave them our baskets they invited us to sit down with them at the kitchen table and share everything we'd brought. My scones and strawberry jam just flew! And then they poured out sweet wine and little biscuits to dip into it, and in the end we all had a bit of a party.'

'And since when do you speak Italian, Sophia?'

'Don't be funny, Dawid. Rome isn't in the sticks, you know. They all speak English very nicely. The children learnt it at school and the parents picked it up from the tourists. That's how they heard about Corriebush. A tourist told them. Fancy that. And what a happy family Dawie! Full of the joys. They're going to open a lovely shop, much smarter than fish.'

'Selling what?'

'All the exotics. Polony and ham and cheese and spaghetti. And you should just see Rosa.'

'Rosa?'

'The daughter. Nineteen years old and nothing short of a madonna. Black hair to her waist, eyes like pools and teeth like sapphires.'

'You mean pearls, Sophia.'

'That's right, pearls. The young men are going to buzz around like flies.'

In no time the exuberant Castello family became part of the Corriebush community and the shop began to thrive. Luigi loved to stand in the doorway, plump as a salami in his long, white apron.

'Hey Missus! Come have a taste!'

Then he'd carve a slice off a ham or a hunk of cheese and offer it on the tip of his long knife. Rosa was always there, keeping an eye on the small boys, while the grandmother sat quietly folded on a stool in the corner and Mrs Castello hung strands of fresh spaghetti over racks to dry, or stirred the chunky soups and pasta sauces that bubbled on the stove in the corner. Soon, Italian dishes were appearing on dinner tables all over town, and everyone agreed that the Castellos were the best thing ever to have come out of Italy.

'Better even than Mona Lisa,' remarked Lily.

'Much better than Mona Lisa,' said Sophia.

'Talented too. The principal of the primary school says those three boys are as bright as buttons. They'll go a long way, he says.'

'And there are two more to come, of course.'

'I wonder how the mother manages.'

'It's what they call the Latin temperature.'

'Temperament.'

'That's what I said. Temperament. Eat, laugh and be merry. Haven't you noticed how nothing bothers Mrs Castello? Even the washing. When her lines are full, she just hangs it all over the pear tree. Sometimes the garden looks like a circus tent.'

'We could learn a thing or two from people like that.'

When Rosa's twenty-first birthday approached, her parents invited the whole town to a celebratory party.

The women discussed it over tea one afternoon.

'It'll be a bit of a squash, but never mind, such lovely people and the food will be good, and of course Rosa will look like an angel.'

'My Daniel says she has a figure like Rubens,' Amelia told them, a trifle smugly. 'A figure like Rubens and a complexion like marble.'

'My goodness Amelia! How does he know?'

'Someone once gave him a calendar of famous oils.'

'Oils? Oh oils! Of course!' and they sipped their tea thoughtfully.

On the night of the party the little shop was filled to bursting. Guests spilled over into the kitchen, even up the stairs and into the street. Under the pear tree in the garden a table stood buckling under the weight of food and bottles of wine.

Sophia filled her plate and found Maria and Anna sitting on a bench. She motioned them to move up so that she could sit down at one end.

'I'm worried about Rosa,' she said. 'There she goes, such a sweet child, looking like a princess in that red skirt and flowers in her hair, and she's never had a boy.'

'A beau,' said Maria.

'That's right. Never had a beau. What's wrong with the local young men do you think?'

'They go to the shop in their dozens, I know that, and they buy capers and olives and other things they don't even want, just to catch a glimpse of her. But ask her for a date? Not a chance.'

'I think they're nervous. After all, they've never handled a foreign beauty before.'

It wasn't long after this discussion that Rosa married Francois Uys. It was a small ceremony, just the family, in the Catholic church.

'Blow me down with a feather,' said Sophia. 'A small wedding I can understand, after having to pay for that big party and everything, but Francois Uys! I mean, Francois must be pushing fifty if he's a day!'

'I simply don't understand it,' Anna mused.

'Of course he *is* the richest farmer in the district, but that doesn't make him any younger. Hardly a catch for a beauty like Rosa.'

'Not a bad looker, though. When he rides at the horse shows with all his apparatus – I mean those long, shiny boots and a cap and a jacket with a split up the back, he looks a bit like John Wayne.'

'And it wasn't his fault that his fiancée left him high and dry. She just wasn't the farming type. I hear she went on to marry a tycoon and lives in Johannesburg.'

'Well, *I* heard that he sometimes lifts the elbow rather high.'

'Perhaps *that* was the reason, then.'

'Well it may not be true, and we never hold with gossip. I think he was just too upset about his fiancée leaving him to think of anyone else until now. And look what he's finally got. The pick of the bunch!'

Maria, however, was distinctly uneasy about Rosa's betrothal. 'I just don't feel right,' she said darkly. 'Something funny there. I feel it in my bones.'

After the marriage, Rosa seldom came to town.

'She's very busy on the farm,' Luigi told them when they enquired. 'Loves the life, big house, lots of servants, horses to ride, a river for swimming and a man who's really good to her. Of course, he often has to go away to horse shows, but then he brings her presents and she says she doesn't mind staying alone.'

'We really miss her here in the shop,' chipped in Mrs Castello. 'But she's happy, and that's what matters.'

The women were pleased to hear it, but decided they had allowed a decent enough interval to pass, and the time was ripe for them to go and see for themselves.

'First, we must organise our transport.'

'For the six of us we will need two cars and two husbands to drive. That mountain road is very bumpy. We'll have to hold our cakes on our laps. One big pothole, and they're in their glory.'

The day was set, and they had already started baking little treats to take out to Rosa, when a hideous and unexpected thing happened.

Nellie was the first to hear of it. Having run out of walnuts for her cookies, she went to the shop; Castello's always stocked them, fresh and shelled. Rosa was sitting in the kitchen with her mother. They were both sobbing, their heads in their hands, and did not even look up when the little bell tinkled. Luigi was behind the counter, wiping his eyes with his apron.

'Luigi?'

'Nellie. It's Francois. He was thrown by his horse.'

After the funeral Rosa went back to the farm, Springfontein.

'She wants to.' Mrs Castello raised her hands, palms upwards, shrugging. 'Perhaps it's best, for a while. She says she's got things to keep her busy. Lots of animals to look after, and kind neighbours. Perhaps after a few weeks she would love you to visit.'

'Of course.'

They were sitting in the lounge at Springfontein, the ladies and Rosa. The two husbands who had done the driving had gone to smoke their pipes by the river after Rosa had shown them all round the farm, the stables, her flower garden, the river in which willow branches dabbled and in which she loved to swim. Now they were going to have tea. Rosa was pale, but composed. It was when Anna called her Rosatjie that she unexpectedly broke down. They let her cry, knowing there was much that she needed to talk about.

'Frans was really good to me,' Rosa began. 'I know you're all wondering how it came about that I married him.'

'We know he was wonderful with horses,' Lily said, thinking to help her along.

'And this is a lovely home,' Anna added.

'And the young men in Corriebush were shy of you, so perhaps you were lonely?'

'We know Francois often came to the shop. He was a cheese lover, I believe?' Rosa nodded.

'So you met him there and got talking and so on, and then one day he brought you out to the farm and asked you to marry him, perhaps under the willows at the river?'

Rosa nodded again.

'Well, we understand all that. But Rosatjie, why did you say yes?'

'Money.'

'Money?' Lily and Anna repeated simultaneously.

'Yes, money,' replied Rosa.

'My goodness. Now I don't know what to say,' said Maria.

Nor did the others. Shocked into silence, they fixed their eyes on the patterned carpet, and sat waiting. Rosa started to explain.

They were a close family, she told them. It was like that in Italy. Whole generations lived together, supporting and depending on each other. Being the eldest of the children she felt a particular responsibility to her parents and her brothers.

'And so I married Frans because my father was having a big problem paying for my brothers' education. Five of them, remember, and both my father and mother were working dreadfully hard. Pappa is getting old now, and sometimes he would just sit with his head in his hands and I could not stand to see him like that. I did not know what to do, I had not thought of a plan, but when Frans asked me to marry him I knew it was the answer to the problem.'

'But child,' Nellie found her voice. 'Rosa dearie, how did you think this would help?'

'He told me he would look after me and my family as well.'

'And you believed him?'

'Yes. I told him I would marry him if he would give me a certain amount of money each month for my family, and he did not hesitate.'

'And did he? Did he keep his word?'

'Never broke it, not once. Frans didn't hold with banks, you know. He kept his money under the bed. At the end of every month he would unlock the trunk, take out a bundle of notes, and give them to me. He would squeeze my hand and say it was my salary. And I would take it to town and give it to Pappa and say I was doing really well, churning bucketfuls of our Guernsey cream, and selling fresh farm butter at the market. I don't think he ever suspected a thing.'

'And how were matters – you know, *matters,* like foxtrot and so on – between you and your Francois?'

'Good, except that he was often away riding at shows … he was one of the best show jumpers in the country, you know. Sometimes he took me with him, but I really felt out of it, especially when some of his old friends asked if I was his daughter. I was happier here. Also, when he was away he would drink a little too much. I think that was why he came off his horse.'

'Oh dear oh dear oh dear,' Amelia sighed. 'What a horrible thing we have here. Will you stay on the farm all alone?'

'Oh yes. The staff is very good, and I can make a steady income.'

'But my child, you're twenty-two. This is no place for a young woman like you. Don't you get lonely? Won't you come back to Corriebush?'

'Yes and no, Auntie Mel. Yes, I do get lonely, but no, I won't come back. At any rate not until my father has enough money in the bank for my brothers, and his old age. Frans left the farm to me, and I know I can make it work. I miss him, though…' her voice trailed off and she looked at them sadly.

When they left, Rosa waved to them from the lawn in front of the gracious old homestead. The women called their husbands back from the river, and they drove to town without saying much, except that they had accomplished their mission.

'So what happens next?' Servaas wanted to know.

'We must wait for a suitable period, maybe several months, before taking action. It's the proper thing to do.'

They were sitting over tea on Nellie's stoep. Lily introduced the subject.

'It is our duty to present her with a man.'

'But there isn't a single one in Corriebush. You can't offer a young boy still wet behind the ears, after all.'

'There's Samuel,' Maria offered.

'Him? The one with the dress?'

'It's not a dress, Maria. It's called a smock, and proper artists wear them so that their clothes don't get spattered.'

Samuel had arrived in Corriebush in a caravan, which he parked next to the river just outside the town. At first they had thought he was some sort of tourist passing through, but after several weeks had gone by and he was still there, they decided to find out exactly what his intentions were.

'But how do you call on a caravan?' they mused. 'There's no front gate, no doorstep, do we just stand on the bank of the river and shout, Yoo-hoo?'

'Just so. And if that doesn't work, we'll throw stones into the water.'

So they filled a basket with home-baked treats and, late one afternoon, strolled down to the river. They found Samuel outside his caravan, sitting on a chair in front of an easel, painting the sunset. When he saw them approaching, he rose and put his brush down.

'No need to look so alarmed,' Anna told him reassuringly. 'We've just come to say, Welcome to Corriebush.' She handed him the basket.

'A little something for your supper.'

'How very kind,' Samuel replied. He lifted the cloth. 'All my favourite things. Would you like to sit down?'

The women looked round, and declined. 'The grass is a bit damp at this time of day,' Lily replied. 'So we'll just be off and hope to see you soon.'

Samuel lifted his broad-brimmed hat and gave a slight bow. 'Your town is beautiful, and so are you, ladies.'

For a moment they were nonplussed, then Maria found her voice.

'Well, *arrivederci* then, as they say.'

Samuel waved them up the bank and then sat down again at his easel with the basket beside him.

'He's really strange, that one.'

'Polite though.'

'I still say he looks like a clown in that dress.'

'I don't know so much. With that little pointed beard and his fine moustache he's not unlike Leonardo.'

'Leonardo?'

'You know, the famous artist. Also Italian, like Rosa.'

'Oh yes, *that* Leonardo.'

'Or Michelangelo,' Amelia chipped in.

'Yes, him too.'

'Well, I say whatever he looks like – Leonardo, Michelwhatshisname or even Chopin – he's definitely what you would call a bit *odd*.'

'Odd or not, Daniel says he's an asset to Corriebush, because dealers are coming from all over the district to buy his paintings. He signs them Samuel D, in the right-hand corner, and one day they might be worth a fortune.'

'Maybe. But in the meantime we have to decide about him and Rosa.'

'He does seem a gentleman. No harm in him, and clever in his way. Perhaps we could get something going.'

'I think we should have a little dinner party. We'll invite him, and put him next to Rosa at the table, and see what happens. Perhaps the sparks will fly.'

'Who knows? It just might work.'

It didn't.

Rosa was at her most beautiful. She wore a low-cut white muslin blouse, a gold chain and dangly earrings, and she had swept her hair up so that it hung down in ringlets onto her bare shoulders. They made a striking couple, she and Samuel, sitting there side by side in the candlelight, and they were as quiet as mice. Just after the soup and before the roast, Rosa turned to him and asked about his painting, and he told her that Karoo landscapes were his speciality. Then, just before the pudding, Samuel asked her whether she had Liliaceae growing on her farm. She said she thought so, after which he quietly enjoyed his dinner, filled Rosa's glass when necessary, admired Lily's centrepiece of flowers and took his leave soon after coffee.

The women were mortified, and came together the following day to discuss the affair.

'We'll have to think of another plan. Perhaps he's too shy, with all of us around. We must get them together, alone.'

'I've got it!'

'What, Sophia?'

'Rosa must have a party on the farm, and we'll all go, and Samuel too.'

'He can't go up those mountains in a caravan.'

'We'll offer him a lift. Tell him we won't take no for an answer, that he can take his paints along and we'll set off early and he can do the sunset and the Liliawhatchamacallit. That'll do it, the sunset and the whatsitsname, and some wine and a good dinner.'

'Especially if we can find a way of leaving them quite alone. Even half an hour might be quite enough.'

Somewhat to their surprise, Samuel agreed.

'I told you, he's a gentleman underneath. He looked quite pleased.'

'Shame. I feel quite bad when I think of our plan. About what we're going to do out there.'

'Nonsense. We're doing it for Rosa. In the end Samuel will thank us.'

'Do you think we should tell our husbands about you know what?'

Anna thought for a while. 'Yes,' she finally decided. 'Else they might produce the missing tool, and spoil the whole game.'

When Lily and Herman stopped to pick Samuel up, he stepped out of his caravan wearing a white silk shirt, tight black trousers, a kerchief loosely knotted round his neck, and a jaunty black hat on his head. There was no sign of his easel.

'Looks like a flaming dancer,' she whispered to her husband.

'Flamenco, Lily.'

'That, or a bandit.'

Samuel greeted them affably, thanked them for their trouble, and sat silently in the back seat until Lily, who was delighted to have this chance to ask a few questions, opened the conversation.

'You're sure of a good meal tonight,' she started off, turning her head to look at him squarely. 'Rosa's a wonderful cook.'

Samuel smiled. She tried again.

'What are you painting at the moment?'

'A landscape.'

'That's nice.'

'We're getting nowhere,' muttered Herman and in a very loud voice shot off a direct question. 'Samuel, tell us straight. We're all wondering. What are you up to, coming to Corriebush in a caravan? Sitting there on the grass all day on a stool with a brush?'

Surprisingly, Samuel spent the rest of the journey telling them exactly what they had been longing to know.

Speaking slowly, in his deep, gentle voice, he started by describing his childhood on his father's farm near the Kruger National Park. He had loved the outdoor life, but had absolutely no interest in growing crops or breeding cattle. Right from the time he had been a small boy he had wanted to paint, wandering around the farm with his sketch pad and pencil. His parents were horrified. Being their only son, they had always assumed he would go to Agricultural College and then take over the farm when his father retired.

'But it was my ambition to study painting and design at a technical college. They said painting pretty pictures was no work for a man, and so I left home and paid for my studies by working in a restaurant at night.'

The course lasted three years, after which he set off on his own, travelling and selling his work wherever he could. 'I was happy and fulfilled and slowly gaining a reputation by the time I reached Corriebush.'

He had not, he said, intended settling here, but found it so peaceful a place with so much scope for his brush that he had decided to stay for as long as it suited him. 'A man with unfulfilled ambitions is like a blown egg. Empty and ready to crack.'

'That's what I always say. Empty and ready to crack,' nodded Lily.

They were the first to arrive at Springfontein. The sun was just setting, the aroma of roasting lamb was in the air, and the lights that Rosa had strung in the trees were beginning to glow and light up the farmyard.

As she came out to meet them, the rest of the party drove up, a whole convoy of cars arriving in a miasma of dust, hooters blaring, women waving, the drivers throwing screeching turns before coming to a halt in front of the stables. When they peeled out of their cars and trooped inside it was a sight to make even the stars smile: a clutch of excited, party-dressed women, all powdered and rouged and chattering like guineafowl. Their plump, capable legs were squeezed into nylon stockings like sausages into casings, they had all been to Hannah's Hairdressing Salon to have their hair done, and their sweetness and laughter and perfume simply filled the night. Sophia tripped going up the steps. 'It's these *blerrie* high heels,' she said. 'I usually only wear them to church.'

'Come Samuel,' said Servaas, taking him by the elbow. 'Once we get past this lot we can have a brandy.'

The dining room was vast in the way that old farmhouse dining rooms always are, with a table that ran from end to end. Rosa, looking as inviting as a ripe peach, positioned herself at the top, and suggested that they all choose a chair and sit down.

'This is it,' Lily whispered.

'Samuel,' she trilled, 'you sit up there, next to Rosa, because you're the youngest man here and we'll need you to jump up and pass the bottles and things.'

It was too late. Servaas had already taken up the chair on Rosa's left, and Daniel was about to sit down on her right.

'I think I'm going to cry,' said Lily.

'All is not lost,' whispered Anna. 'We still have our trump card in hand.'

The evening passed pleasantly enough, with much noisy conversation and clinking of glasses. But it was going nowhere with Samuel and Rosa, for they were seated at opposite ends.

Just before coffee was served, Anna winked at Lily, and then stood up, saying quite unashamedly, 'Excuse me, it's the powder room for me.'

Shortly after that, Lily followed. They met outside, in the dark, next to the stables where all the cars were parked.

'I think this is how it is done,' Lily muttered, bending down. 'Yes, just a gentle twist. Now we'll do the rest.'

And one by one they visited each car, crouched down and loosened the valves on twenty-four wheels. Sighing gently as the air was released, the tyres settled onto the dusty ground with a whoof and a clunk.

'There now. Flat on the ground like sleeping cows,' said Lily, as they dusted their hands and went back for coffee.

Just after midnight, Herman pushed back his chair. 'A toast to Rosa, our hostess. We would all like to stay till morning, Rosatjie, but duty calls. Thank you from us all for a grand evening!'

And they all raised their glasses, collected their coats, kissed Rosa warmly, and left. The men looked sleepy. The women were all smiling with their secret.

'And now?' Servaas stepped back and looked at his back tyre. He bent down and prodded it, then crawled all around and tested each one, swearing more loudly with each discovery.

'What's up?'

'Flat as pancakes. Every damn one.'

Herman checked his. 'Dammit Servaas! So are mine!'

'And mine! What's going on here? Anybody got a jack?'

The men looked concerned and shook their heads, exactly as their wives had told them to.

And then Rosa nearly spoilt everything by saying, 'I think Frans had a jack.'

They held their breath.

'But it's somewhere in the workshop and it's too dark to see in there now.'

'Oh much too dark,' Anna said quickly. 'We'll just have to go on with the party, won't we? Can't travel with flat tyres, can we? Might as well party a little longer and hit the road when the sun comes up. If you can have us to stay a little longer, Rosa? Any more coffee?'

Rosa was delighted, and gleefully they all returned to the dining room, which was looking a little dishevelled now with the dirty plates and crumpled napkins and half-dead candles.

'What about a bit of dancing, Rosatjie?' suggested Herman. 'I see you have a gramophone in the corner there.'

'Ah yes, I've got some records Pappa gave me – there's Cosi fan tutte and The Barber of Seville and some Verdi.'

They tried a whirl or two, but it wasn't the sort of music they were used to.

'*Ag*, no Rosa. If you have a spare room or two we'll just go and lie down for a while, it's close to sunrise anyway, and it's such a warm night, we'll just lie down on top of the quilts so you won't have to wash anything.'

Rosa showed the couples her rooms and gratefully they marched off and flopped down on the beds. Samuel and Rosa were left alone.

'It's working,' Lily said to Herman as she kicked off her shoes and lay down.

'It's working,' Sophia told Dawid and Nellie told Charlie, Amelia told Daniel and Anna told James.

'If Samuel doesn't grab his chance now, in the dining room, he never will,' Maria said to Servaas. 'He'll never find another woman like Rosa, with her looks and sweetness and all those Lilythings to paint when he chooses.'

Of course, not one of them ever found out exactly what happened between Rosa and Samuel in those pre-dawn hours in the Springfontein dining room. But what they saw when they eventually trooped in just after sunrise was enough to tell them that their plan had been successful.

Rosa's eyes were dancing and Samuel's neckerchief was skew. They were sitting side by side with cups of cold coffee in front of them. Samuel's head was bent towards Rosa and he was talking earnestly, while she was taking small bites out of a pear. The juice was running down her chin and down her neck, and she did not move to wipe it away.

'I saw that once in a movie,' whispered Anna. 'It means there's electricity there.'

'He's got her hand under the table,' whispered Lily.

'*Shhhh*, woman.' Herman nudged her in the ribs.

But just then Rosa saw them and jumped up. 'The jack!' she exclaimed.

And in no time, six cars were churning up the dust road back to Corriebush. Samuel was not with them. The women were elated. 'The signs could not be better.'

When they married a few months later, Rosa sold the farm and they bought Corriebush Number Five. Samuel left his caravan at the river so that people could go there and use it for picnics, and he and Rosa opened a restaurant right next door to Castello's. They called the restaurant Casa Castello, specialising in pasta dinners. Spaghetti Carbonara, Taglierini with Mushrooms, Ravioli with Spinach, Risottos and Lasagnes, Flat Breads and Sorbets.

'All the exotics, just like her father,' said Maria.

'A chip off the old Italian block,' put in Sophia.

Casa Castello was a success from the start. Rosa cooked and Samuel carried on painting and hung his works on the walls, and word spread as far as Port Elizabeth, Graaff-Reinet, and beyond. People came to eat, and to buy. It was all just the most wonderful happiness – for Rosa, for Samuel, for Pappa and Mamma and the boys. And for the women of Corriebush, whose carefully laid plans had, quite magically, worked out, it was a triumph.

Rosa never forgot the generosity of her first husband, and always spoke of him with gentle affection. The boys' education was assured, and Luigi and Mrs could slow down a bit.

'Rosa is a shining star,' Sophia declared, emotionally wiping away a tear or two. 'Nothing less than a shining star in our little community. In Italy they would make a statue of her.'

'With a fountain.'

'In the middle of Rome.'

And they lifted their teacups and toasted the day the Italians had come to town.

ROSA'S RECIPES

When Rosa cooked, the sensual aromas that escaped from her kitchen at Casa Castello wafted right through the streets of Corriebush. These were not ordinary cooking smells, they were perfumes: garlic melting into hot butter, herbs frittering in olive oil, fish baking with fennel, tomatoes grilling, mozzarella spreading … In true Italian tradition, Rosa cooked with love and enthusiasm. She had the utmost respect for good, fresh ingredients, and this meant that her menu had to be kept quite short, but her creations were so richly flavoured, colourful and inviting, that diners were always happy with her choices of the day. In fact, the Corriebush community filled the little restaurant night after night, and very soon learnt to eat as the Italians do: with enormous passion. This was coupled with a great deal of noise, as they discovered the joys of bean soups and pastas, of creamy risottos and meaty casseroles, brilliant salads and dreamy desserts, while Rosa flitted from kitchen to candle-lit tables, and Samuel took the orders. Everything was perfect, but for one thing – they just wouldn't go home. Because everyone knew everyone else, they constantly called to their friends from one end of the room to the other, passing bottles of wine from table to table, and even plates of food that someone wanted someone else to try. And even though Rosa and Samuel were often exhausted by midnight, they did not mind, knowing that animation is the heart of the Italian meal. They would simply sit in a corner, sipping cappuccinos and waiting for Sophia – it was always Sophia – to raise her hand and trill 'Ag, Rosatjie, before I leave, just one more little helping of that lovely Sam and Freddie.'

'Semifreddo, Sophia.'

'That's what I said, Dawid.'

Chunky Vegetable-Pasta Soup with Pesto Toasts

A really robust soup, this one, and spot-on for supper on a cold night.
The addition of borlotti beans is optional, but they're just *so* good in affirming
the Italian theme – if unobtainable, use cannellinis. The pesto toasts are not served separately,
but plopped into the bowls before adding the soup, and the whole affair adds up to a buxom,
full-flavoured meal-in-a-bowl. Finish off with a leafy salad, or fresh fruit,
or lovely, munchy biscotti with coffee.

30 ml (2 Tbsp) olive oil
1 large onion, finely chopped
3 cloves garlic, crushed
2 sticks table celery (remove any stringy sides), plus leaves, chopped
2 medium carrots, diced
200 g courgettes (baby marrows), pared and diced
5 ml (1 tsp) dried oregano
1.5 litres (6 cups) chicken or vegetable stock (or even water)
125 ml (½ cup) tomato purée
sea salt and a good sprinkling of sugar
2–3 bay leaves
60 g (a heaped ½ cup) small pasta shells
250 ml (1 cup) finely shredded spinach, or torn baby spinach leaves
1 x 410 g can borlotti beans, drained and rinsed
a small handful of fresh coriander leaves
baguettes or ciabatta, diagonally sliced
basil pesto

Heat the oil in a large, deep saucepan and soften the onion. Add the garlic, celery, carrots, courgettes and oregano, and toss until just starting to soften and smell enticing. Add the stock, tomato purée, seasoning and sugar, and bay leaves. Bring to the boil, then cover and simmer until the vegetables are soft – about 30 minutes. Add the pasta and spinach, and simmer for 10 minutes. Add the beans and coriander and heat through. Remove the bay leaves and check seasoning. Some time before the soup is ready, toast the bread on both sides, and spread lightly with basil pesto. To serve, place a slice on the bottom of each (deep) soup bowl, ladle the soup over, and serve with parmesan for sprinkling. **Serves 6.**

SIMPLE SEAFOOD SOUP WITH ARBORIO RICE AND PISTOU

The list of ingredients is quite long, but this is a really easy soup to make –
the one essential being a *good* fish stock. As it's a chunky, filling soup,
it can be served as a main course, followed by a salad and/or fresh fruit.

30 ml (2 Tbsp) olive oil and
a pat of butter
1 large onion, finely chopped
1 large leek, finely sliced
2 medium carrots, finely diced
1 large stick table celery,
plus leaves, chopped
3 cloves garlic, crushed
1 x 5 cm strip lemon peel
2 bay leaves
75 ml (5 Tbsp) arborio rice (uncooked)
60 ml (¼ cup) white wine
1 x 410 g can peeled, diced tomatoes,
plus juice
1 litre (4 cups) hot fish stock
sea salt and a little sugar to taste
400–450 g skinless
white fish fillets, cubed
about 300 g mussels on the half-shell,
thawed if frozen
a handful of chopped flat-leaf parsley
basil pesto for topping

Heat the oil and butter in a large, deep saucepan. Soften the onion and leek, then add the carrots, celery, garlic, lemon peel, bay leaves, rice and wine. Toss for about 5 minutes to sweat and coat the rice, then add the tomatoes, stock and seasoning and sugar. Bring to the boil, then cover and simmer for about 30 minutes. Add the fish, mussels and parsley, and simmer, half-covered, just until the fish is cooked. Remove the bay leaves and lemon peel and check seasoning. Serve in deep bowls (not soup plates) with a small dollop of pesto (or pistou, seeing that it's in soup), a plate for the mussel shells, and plenty of bread for dipping. **Serves 4 generously.**

Layered Tuna, Bean and Egg Salad

An unsophisticated salad, effortless, quickly put together, and a complete meal.
Served with a tumble of hot Italian rolls, a decanter of Instant Herbed Oil (see below)
for dipping, and a bowl of salad leaves with rocket, it slots happily into informal alfresco dining.

600 g ripe but firm tomatoes, sliced into rings

a sprinkling of sugar

milled sea salt and black pepper

1 bunch spring onions, chopped

a small handful of fresh basil leaves, roughly torn

2 x 410 g cans cannellini beans, rinsed, drained and patted dry

2 x 150 or 170 g cans shredded tuna in oil*

15–30 ml (1–2 Tbsp) balsamic vinegar

45 ml (3 Tbsp) olive oil (the best – cold-pressed, extra virgin)

4 hard-boiled eggs, sliced into rings

chopped flat-leaf parsley

Layer the ingredients in the given order (that is, starting with the tomatoes and carrying straight on) on a large platter with slightly raised sides. Make just one layer of each ingredient, spreading evenly, or drizzling, when using the vinegar and oil. Cover loosely and stand for about 30 minutes before serving. **Serves 4 generously.**

* Tuna in water can be used, if preferred, but drain it well; or use one can in oil, and one can in water, and adjust the quantity of olive oil accordingly.

Instant herbed oil

No need to bottle and store this one – once cooled, pour into a spouted decanter and pass for individual drizzling. Use a heavy-based saucepan, small but *deep* (for safety's sake) and into it put 150 ml (⅗ cup) olive oil, and the same of canola or sunflower oil; 2 sprigs fresh rosemary and 4 sprigs fresh thyme (about 10 cm each); 2 crumbled bay leaves; 2 fresh sage leaves, bruised, and 2 cloves garlic, peeled and lightly smashed. Stir to moisten the herbs, then heat slowly until just popping, *not* boiling. Leave to pop very gently for 6–8 minutes, giving the occasional stir to bruise the herbs, until the aroma is blissfully aromatic. Remove from the stove, leave it to stop hissing and cool down, then strain.

CALAMARI ON SHELLS

Serve this silky calamari on pasta shells in pasta bowls.
It isn't quite a soup, nor a sauce, but a sort of rich calamari broth
with a waft of tangy gremolata. Add a basket of crusty rolls,
and follow with a salad for a lovely, lusty meal.

1 kg cleaned calamari tubes
1 x 410 g can chopped tomatoes
60 ml (¼ cup) dry white wine
10 ml (2 tsp) tomato paste
10 ml (2 tsp) soft brown sugar
2 ml (½ tsp) each paprika,
dried oregano and sea salt
30 ml (2 Tbsp) olive oil
1 large onion, finely chopped
125 ml (½ cup) fish or chicken stock
3 bay leaves
15 ml (1 Tbsp) soft butter
15 ml (1 Tbsp) flour
250 g small pasta shells
For the GREMOLATA: mix a handful of
chopped, flat-leaf parsley with a
crushed clove of garlic and the finely
grated rind of ½ lemon

Slit the calamari tubes down one side, open out flat, remove any spiny bits that might have been left behind, then cut across into thin strips. Dry as thoroughly as possible. Whizz the tomatoes, wine, tomato paste, sugar, paprika, oregano and salt in a blender. Heat the oil in a *deep*, wide-based saucepan. Add the onion and, when golden, add the calamari. Keep tossing just until it stiffens and turns white, then reduce the heat immediately, pour over the blended tomato sauce and the fish stock, and slip in the bay leaves. Simmer over very low heat, stirring occasionally and keeping the lid of the saucepan tilted, for about 1 hour, by which time the calamari should be very tender and the sauce mellow and plentiful. To thicken it for coating the pasta, mash the butter and flour to a paste and stir small pats into the sauce, then sprinkle with the gremolata. Heat for a few minutes, uncovered, to mingle all the flavours, then ladle into the bowls over the cooked pasta.
Serves 4.

Citrus Chicken Bake with Minted Pesto Pasta

This unusual combination – savoury, orangy chicken and pasta shells whiffed with fresh mint – comes as a wonderful culinary surprise. Deliciously different, yet perfectly straightforward, it's simply an exciting new way of treating good, basic ingredients.

900 g–1 kg free-range chicken pieces, trimmed of excess fat
30 ml (2 Tbsp) olive oil
3–4 cloves garlic, chopped
2 pickling onions, chopped
1 sprig of fresh rosemary, leaves chopped (about 15 ml (1 Tbsp))
150 ml (⅗ cup) fresh orange juice
coarsely grated rind of ½ orange
30 ml (2 Tbsp) honey
45 ml (3 Tbsp) white vermouth
15 ml (1 Tbsp) whole grain mustard
coarsely grated rind of 1 medium lemon
5 ml (1 tsp) sea salt
200 g pasta shells

Remove and discard the wing tips, they just get in the way. Arrange the chicken pieces, fleshy side down, fitting closely in a dish suitable for marinating and baking. Whizz all the remaining ingredients, except the pasta, in a blender, and pour over the chicken. Leave for 30 minutes. Cover with a lid, or greaseproof paper and then a sheet of foil, and bake at 180 °C for 45 minutes. Turn and bake, uncovered, for a further 35–40 minutes until the chicken is tender and brown. Skim off the fat. Cook the pasta, then drain it in a colander set over a bowl. Return the pasta to the saucepan with a spoon of the cooking water, and stir in just enough pesto to gloss and flavour. Serve immediately. Drizzle the sauce over each serving of chicken and spoon the pasta alongside. **Serves 4.**

Pesto

250 ml (1 cup) fresh mint leaves (about 10 g), rinsed and dried
250 ml (1 cup) parsley tufts, firmly packed (about 20 g)
20 g walnuts, roughly chopped
30 ml (2 Tbsp) freshly grated parmesan or pecorino cheese
1 clove garlic, chopped
90 ml (6 Tbsp) olive oil

Place all the ingredients, except the oil, in the bowl of a processor fitted with the metal blade. Pulse until finely chopped, then slowly drizzle in the oil, scraping down the sides – the pesto should be thick and chunky, not smooth.

Karoo Bolognese

... in which our local big bird is given some foreign treatment and a very long simmer. The result will be a jolly good pasta sauce, not as succulent as when made with beef or lamb or pork (as in Italy), but lean and healthy and a good ethnic alternative.

30 ml (2 Tbsp) oil
15 ml (1 Tbsp) butter
1 large onion, finely chopped
1 stick table celery, plus leaves, finely chopped
1 medium carrot, finely diced
500 g ostrich mince
2–3 cloves garlic, crushed
80 ml (⅓ cup) red wine
250 ml (1 cup) tomato purée
500 ml (2 cups) hot beef stock
sea salt, milled black pepper and a little sugar to taste
about 60 ml (4 Tbsp) flat-leaf or curly parsley, chopped
2 ml (½ tsp) dried oregano
2 bay leaves
grated parmesan

Heat the oil and butter in a large saucepan. Add the vegetables and stir over low heat until beginning to soften. Add the mince and the garlic, and brown well over medium heat – toss continually to 'loosen' the mince, breaking up any clumps and lumps. Add the wine and simmer until evaporated, and only the fragrance lingers, then stir in the remaining ingredients. Reduce the heat to very low and simmer, half-covered, for about 1½ hours, stirring now and then, and adding, if necessary, a little extra stock in order to end up with a thick, rich-looking brown sauce. Remove the bay leaves, ladle the sauce onto servings of spaghetti and top with grated parmesan. **Serves 4 generously.**

LEMONY VEAL ESCALOPES

If you buy escalopes, they will need to be flattened with a mallet or rolling pin,
so it makes sense to buy schnitzels in the first place. These are easy to find,
and schnitzel is simply the Austrian word for a very thin escalope (or scallopine),
so it boils down to the same thing really – a thin slice of veal, ready to be used
in this luscious, lemony, quick dish. If doubling up, you'll need
a jumbo frying pan – otherwise use two pans to avoid crowding.

30 ml (2 Tbsp) flour

4 fresh young sage leaves, finely chopped

4 veal schnitzels (about 270 g total weight)

30 ml (2 Tbsp) olive oil

a pat of butter

sea salt to taste

60 ml (¼ cup) white vermouth

175 ml (⅔ cup) chicken stock

7 ml (1½ tsp) rinsed, chopped capers

30 ml (2 Tbsp) finely chopped flat-leaf parsley

2 ml (½ tsp) very finely grated lemon rind

10 ml (2 tsp) butter

Mix the flour and sage and use to coat both sides of the veal. Heat the oil and butter in a frying pan wide enough to take the schnitzels in a single layer. Fry quickly on both sides until just cooked and golden brown, then transfer to a plate and season. Reduce the heat and pour the vermouth into the pan. Reduce by half, then add the stock, capers, parsley and lemon rind, all mixed together. Simmer for 2–3 minutes while enjoying the lovely lemony whiff, then swirl in the butter and return the veal just to heat through – don't overcook, as the schnitzels will toughen. Serve at once with the juices poured over, and lemon wedges for squeezing. **Serves 4 modestly.**

The Simplest Vegetable Pasta

When you read the recipe you'll see how easy it is, and when you taste it
you'll know that it's one you'll turn to often: a couple of ingredients,
a couple of minutes, and there you have a salubrious tangle of spinach fettucine
with in-and-out-of-the-pan vegetables. Lots of flavour, little effort, and profoundly useful.

30 ml (2 Tbsp) olive oil
2 cloves garlic, crushed
6 spring onions, chopped
250 g large white mushrooms,
wiped and sliced
1 red pepper, seeded and julienned
120 g baby spinach, roughly torn
2 ml (½ tsp) grated nutmeg
30 ml (2 Tbsp) white vermouth
200 g spinach fettucine,
cooked and drained
a few fresh basil leaves, torn
a little sea salt
45 ml (3 Tbsp) butter
45 ml (3 Tbsp) grated parmesan
or pecorino cheese

Mix the oil, all the vegetables, the nutmeg and
vermouth in a large saucepan. Heat, and toss for
a few minutes, until just beginning to wilt. Add
the fettucine, and toss together lightly, adding the
basil, salt, butter and cheese. Simply super served
with extra grated cheese, a flat bread topped
with tomatoes and olives, and a green salad –
undressed, but pass some good olive oil for
those who want it. **Serves 4.**

FAST FUSILLI WITH ROCKET AND ROASTED GARLIC

… and broccoli and cherry tomatoes – all cooked in one pot.
This is a really good answer to the quest for fast food that manages to be both tasty
and trendy. If you roast the garlic in the oven at the same time that you're heating
the ciabatta and at the same time that you're cooking the pasta,
supper will be ready in under 30 minutes.

250–275 g fusilli or farfalle
300 g broccoli florets, halved
400 g cherry tomatoes, slit on one
side, but not cut through
a *large* handful each rocket and baby
spinach leaves, rinsed and dried
about 15 ml (1 Tbsp) basil pesto
60 ml (4 Tbsp) olive oil
60 ml (4 Tbsp) grated parmesan
or pecorino
sea salt if necessary
12–16 plump cloves garlic, unpeeled
shaved parmesan to serve

Cook the pasta as usual, in a large, deep saucepan with lots of water, a little salt and a dash of oil. Shortly before it's done *al dente*, drop in the broccoli and tomatoes, return to the boil and, after a few minutes, when the broccoli looks tender, drain in a colander and tip everything into a large, warmed serving dish. Quickly mix in the rocket, spinach, pesto, olive oil and cheese. Check seasoning and serve with the garlic (see below) and hot, crusty Italian bread and shaved parmesan. **Serves 4 modestly.**

Roasted garlic

Place the separated cloves (unpeeled, but loose, papery skin removed) in a small ovenproof dish. Add a little olive oil, toss to coat and then roast at 200 °C for about 25 minutes until browning and smelling good. Pass them around (along with the shaved parmesan) and allow diners to squeeze the smooth, mellow pulp into their pasta.

Roasted Vegetables in a Creamy Tomato Sauce

This one is for hungry diners: chunky vegetables in a rosy sauce laced with herbs,
bolstered with a can of borlottis, and served on tangles of fettucine.
Put out grated parmesan, a crusty loaf and olive oil, and they'll be happy for hours.

400 g aubergines (brinjals), diced,
dégorged, rinsed and dried
350 g courgettes (baby marrows),
pared and chunked (prepared weight)
2 red peppers, seeded and sliced
into strips
1 large onion, cut into 10 wedges
4 plump cloves garlic, crushed
5 ml (1 tsp) dried oregano
a little sea salt
60 ml (¼ cup) olive oil
about 400 g fettucine

SAUCE

2 x 410 g cans tomatoes (try for
whole Italian), chopped, plus juice
2 medium carrots, diced
1 medium onion, chopped
1 large stick table celery,
plus leaves, chopped
15 ml (1 Tbsp) tomato paste
125 ml (½ cup) red wine
30 ml (2 Tbsp) olive oil
10 ml (2 tsp) sugar and a little sea salt
125 ml (½ cup) fresh basil leaves,
or basil and parsley mixed
1 x 410 g can borlotti beans,
drained and rinsed*

Place all the vegetables in a large baking dish, sprinkle with oregano and salt, toss with the oil and roast, uncovered, at 220 °C for about 40 minutes until soft, sizzling and starting to brown (toss once during the baking period). Meanwhile, make the sauce. Place all the ingredients except for the basil and beans in a very large saucepan, bring to the boil, then cover and simmer over very low heat for about 45 minutes until everything is cooked, and the sauce is intensely red and juicy. Allow to cool down before puréeing in a blender, in batches, until smooth. Return to the saucepan, add the roasted vegetables, and the basil and beans. When piping hot, serve with the just-cooked pasta. If the sauce is really too thick, add just a little stock, but keep it voluptuous.
Serves 6–8.

* If you can't find borlottis, substitute cannellini beans or chickpeas.

Mushroom Risotto with Tassies, Spinach and Pine Nuts

It's moist and creamy with a pinkish tinge (the Tassies), a few threads of green
(the spinach) and – the starring ingredient – chunks of portabellini mushrooms.
These are just lovely in a risotto; they hold their shape and texture and have a matchless,
intense flavour. If unavailable, substitute brown mushrooms; the wine you will find.

900 ml (3⅗ cups) well-seasoned chicken stock

3 cloves garlic, crushed

30 ml (2 Tbsp) olive oil

15 ml (1 Tbsp) butter

1 medium onion, finely chopped

2 rashers lean, unsmoked back bacon (optional)

250 g plump portabellini mushrooms, wiped and quartered

300 ml (1⅕ cups) arborio rice

2 ml (½ tsp) freshly grated nutmeg

150 ml (⅗ cup) Tassenberg (or a dry red of choice)

2 large handfuls (about 60 g) baby spinach

sea salt and milled black pepper

45 ml (3 Tbsp) freshly grated parmesan or pecorino cheese (not packaged)

30–45 ml (2–3 Tbsp) toasted pine nuts

Heat the stock with the garlic (use a saucepan with a lip for easy pouring) and keep the liquid warm on a stove plate set to low. Heat the oil and butter in a wide-based, heavy saucepan, and add the onion and bacon. (In Italy they would use pancetta; substitute bacon, or leave it out altogether.) When the onion turns golden and the bacon (if using) starts frying, add the mushrooms and toss for a few minutes. You'll find that they won't shrink like most mushrooms do, so just cook them briefly before tipping in the rice and the nutmeg. Use a wooden spoon to stir gently until coated, then *slowly* add the red wine. When absorbed, start adding the hot stock – do this in small cupfuls, waiting until each is absorbed before continuing. The whole process takes about 30 minutes. Tear the spinach roughly, add it, together with the seasoning, then remove from the stove – the spinach will wilt almost immediately. Mix in the parmesan and the pine nuts, and stand, covered, for 2 minutes before serving in deep pasta bowls. Pass extra parmesan for sprinkling, a bottle of superior olive oil for those who want it, and serve a plain green salad on the side. **Serves 4.**

WINE-POACHED PEARS WITH GINGER AND WALNUT MASCARPONE

Despite the title this is not a grand dessert, nevertheless, it's delicious,
does not take long to make, and can be done a day ahead and kept in the refrigerator.

375 ml (1½ cups) water
125 ml (½ cup) semi-sweet white wine
125 ml (½ cup) granulated sugar
4 large, firm, unblemished pears
(about 800 g), Packham's or Beurre
Bosc are good choices
fresh lemon juice (optional)
ground cinnamon

Mix the water, wine and sugar in a large frying pan and heat up slowly, stirring now and then to dissolve the sugar, and when you're not stirring, prepare the pears. Peel, halve and core them, then place them in the bubbling syrup, rounded sides up. They should fit the pan snugly. Reduce the heat to very low and simmer gently for about 30 minutes or until soft but still perfectly shaped; test with a sharp skewer. If done, use a slotted spoon to arrange the pears, rounded sides still up, in a shallow serving dish – a 23 cm pie dish is just right. Taste the syrup in the pan, and if it is too sweet, add a dash of lemon juice. Increase the heat and boil, uncovered, until very bubbly and syrupy – a matter of minutes. Pour over the pears, dust lightly with cinnamon, cool, then cover and refrigerate. **Makes at least 4 plump servings.**

Ginger and walnut mascarpone

125 g mascarpone
a few drops of vanilla essence
15 ml (1 Tbsp) sifted icing sugar
15 ml (1 Tbsp) milk
45 ml (3 Tbsp) chopped walnuts
30–45 ml (2–3 Tbsp) finely chopped
preserved ginger

Using an electric hand-held whisk, whisk the mascarpone, vanilla, icing sugar and milk. This takes longer to get results than whipping cream, but it does whip up a lighter mascarpone with increased volume. Fold in the walnuts and ginger and refrigerate. Serve 1–2 pear halves per diner with a dollop of mascarpone at the side, or enlarge the hollows and pile with mascarpone.

Chocolate Frangelico Semifreddo

Semifreddos are very rich, soft, frozen desserts often made with double cream,
eggs and sugar, with a flavouring of choice. This version is not strictly traditional,
but it's hard to beat for sheer, delicious decadence. The mixture is set
in a loaf-shaped container, frozen overnight, turned out and sliced for serving.
It will start to melt almost immediately, which is what it should do,
therefore have serving plates ready and waiting. If you want to set the slices on
a pool of sorts, choose something bland like a fresh pear coulis – even custard
would detract from the intense chocolate flavour. If not using a coulis,
go for one or two sweet, scarlet strawberries – plain, or choc-dipped.
They look fabulous placed alongside each slice.

40–50 g hazelnuts
200 ml (⅘ cup) light brown sugar
125 ml (½ cup) water
175 ml (scant ¾ cup) cocoa powder
3 large free-range eggs, separated
2 ml (½ tsp) vanilla essence
45 ml (3 Tbsp) Frangelico liqueur
250 ml (1 cup) cream, softly whipped
a small pinch of salt

Roast or grill the nuts until browned. Wrap them in a kitchen towel and rub vigorously to remove the loose skins, then chop the nuts coarsely. Place the sugar, water and cocoa powder in a small saucepan and melt over low heat, stirring (do not boil). Set aside to cool for about 10 minutes. Whisk the egg yolks, vanilla essence and liqueur very well until foamy. Gradually add the chocolate mixture, whisking well between additions. Fold in the cream and the nuts. Stiffly whisk *two* of the egg whites (you don't need the third) with the salt. Stir a dollop through the chocolate mixture, then gently fold in the remainder. Line a 1-litre freezerproof, loaf-shaped container with clingfilm (use enough for an overlap), pour in the 'freddo' and freeze at once. After a few hours it should be firm enough to cover the top with the overlapping clingwrap. Freeze for 24 hours. Unmould onto a large, flat plate, slice and serve. **Makes 10–12 slices.**

AMARULA PANNA COTTA

Panna cottas are delicate 'cooked cream' desserts, usually made with
sweetened double cream, flavoured with vanilla, and softly set with just a flurry of gelatine.
Once chilled and unmoulded, they look just like wobbly little blancmanges,
but they're much richer and because of this, a trend – outside of Italy – is to scale down
the fat with the addition of milk, which of course requires extra gelatine,
which could result in a rubbery wobble, which is all wrong. An attractive solution
is to set the panna cottas in small coffee cups. Then, instead of unmoulding them,
you simply place the cups on their saucers, with small spoons alongside.
In this way it is still possible to use a proportion of milk without extra gelatine.
This is an unusual presentation, but these little Amarula creams provide a seriously
delicious ending to a fine dinner when something sweet – but small – would be just right.

10 ml (2 tsp) gelatine
90 ml (6 Tbsp) Amarula liqueur
500 ml (2 cups) thick whipping cream
(or double cream)
250 ml (1 cup) full-cream milk
45 ml (3 Tbsp) castor sugar
a few drops of vanilla essence*
5 ml (1 tsp) each cocoa powder and
icing sugar for topping

*** A split vanilla pod may be the
choice of chefs, but it's pricey,
and not essential.**

Sprinkle the gelatine over the liqueur and leave to sponge. Mix the cream, milk and sugar in a heavy saucepan and slowly bring to just below boiling point. Remove from the stove; briskly stir in the sponged gelatine and give it a quick whisk to make sure it's dissolved. Add the vanilla, pour into a jug and cool, stirring occasionally. Pour into six small coffee cups and refrigerate for a few hours until softly set. Just before serving, mix the cocoa and icing sugar in a small sieve and sift just a whisper over the top of each – this is just to add a little colour to the pale cream. **Serves 6.**

Almond Biscotti with Cherries and Amaretto

Not quite a rusk, not quite a biscuit, but crisp little things to dunk into coffee
or sweet wine after a meal. The flavours have become more and more varied as their
popularity has increased, and I have experimented with walnut and cinnamon, and pistachio
and spice biscotti, but in the end this one seems to remain the favourite. I toast the almonds
for added flavour, and use Amaretto instead of the artificial almond essence sometimes used.

3 large free-range eggs
200 ml (⅘ cup) castor sugar
2 ml (½ tsp) vanilla essence
30 ml (2 Tbsp) Amaretto liqueur
750 ml (3 cups) cake flour
a pinch of sea salt
5 ml (1 tsp) baking powder
2 ml (½ tsp) grated nutmeg
100 g blanched almonds, whole,
slivered or flaked, toasted
12 glacé cherries, rinsed,
dried and chopped

Whisk the eggs, castor sugar, vanilla essence and liqueur very well, until light and creamy. Sift in the flour, salt, baking powder and nutmeg. Using an electric whisk, mix to a soft dough, then gather up and work into a smooth ball with your hands. Place on a lightly floured board. Roll the dough (flouring your hands occasionally, as it can be sticky) into a log, incorporating the nuts and cherries as you go. (If you don't like cherries, leave them out – I add them for their cheerful colour.) The almonds I use are usually the flaked ones, as it is easier to spread them throughout the dough so that in the end each slice contains a few pieces. When all the nuts and cherries are incorporated, divide into 2 logs, each about 24 cm long and 5 cm wide. Lighly oil a large baking sheet and cover the base with baking paper. Place the logs side by side, but apart, as they will puff up in the oven, and flatten gently with your palm. Bake at 160 °C for 30 minutes, until deep cream in colour. Remove from the oven and leave to stand for 5 minutes. Reduce temperature to 140 °C, slice off the pointy ends of logs, then slice the rest into diagonal 1 cm thick slices. Place flat on the sheet and bake for 20 minutes. Turn and bake for a further 20–30 minutes until dry and just beginning to look toasted. Cool on the baking sheet before storing airtight. **Makes 40.**

OLYMPIA

Olympia arrived in Corriebush on Wednesday, the fourth of March, at six o'clock in the evening. Daleen remembered the date exactly because she had just signed the documents concluding a most satisfactory sale. The women of Corriebush had asked her to bid on a vacant plot next to the church.

'We really need a piece of ground where we can put up permanent stalls and a few umbrellas for our bazaars and produce sales,' Anna had explained. 'Then we need not apply to the council every time we want to use the town hall, and we could even have pony rides and hoop-la and that sort of thing.'

The board of church elders had eventually agreed to sell for a most reasonable price, and Daleen knew the ladies would be delighted. But first the haggling, and then the filling in of forms had taxed her nerves, and it was with a huge sense of relief that she closed her office door, stepped onto the pavement and started off briskly in the direction of home.

Right in her path stood a tiny figure. She had her back to Daleen, for her face was turned to the west where the sun was just setting, staining the evening sky in a blush of colours such as one sees only in the Karoo – an explosion of nature's exuberant best in a rumble of purple clouds riffled with gold and whorls of scarlet. And like leaves skittering in a wind, flocks of kestrels spiralled dizzily round the church steeple, swooping and diving in the fiery glow until it was time to nest. It was then that the palette slowly faded, the sun shuddered and fell, and twilight wrapped the town in a soft, grey shawl.

It was a sight that always mesmerized people; few could move away from it, and in the time it took to change from light to dark, the little figure had not stirred. It was only when Daleen approached that it turned, and she saw that it was a frail old lady, dressed in black from head to toe, and crying.

Olympia had arrived in Corriebush by taxi from Port Elizabeth. The driver needed to start on the long journey back before nightfall and so he had simply dropped her, along with her two battered suitcases, on the pavement outside Daleen's office. He told her that this was where she would find the local estate agent, and if she went inside she would get fixed up.

Olympia had nodded and paid him, and then just stood where she was, too nervous and confused to move. When Daleen saw the weary, wrinkled face, the fear in the faded eyes and the tears that slowly trickled down the creased old cheeks, she put her arms round the woman and held her tightly for a moment. Then she smoothed the stray grey hairs that had escaped from beneath her headscarf. 'Come,' she said gently, and picked up the two suitcases. Olympia followed without a word, shuffling along the pavement in tiny boots that flapped and clicked with every step. Her skirt was long and dusty and around her waist she had knotted a thin, faded jersey.

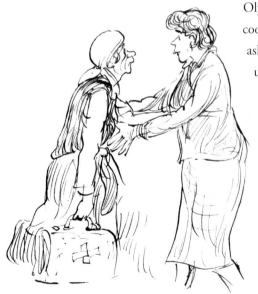

Now, Daleen was a pretty hard businesswoman, but that night she was simply Daleen Bothma, a kind and motherly farmer's daughter. She took Olympia to her little flat, made up a bed in the lounge, cooked a supper of scrambled eggs and sausage, and did not ask a single question. She simply smiled often at her unexpected guest, ran a hot bath for her, and then waited. Olympia's story took until midnight in the telling. She was quite articulate, but sometimes hesitated while she searched for just the right English word. And the deeper she got into her story, the faster Daleen's mind worked, making plans. Firstly, it was obvious that Olympia needed somewhere to stay. A place of her own, where she could live quietly while her extraordinary problems were being sorted out. Mentally, Daleen scrolled through her files – and there it was. Number Six. The cottage had been standing empty for a long time because it was so small that nobody wanted to buy it. The owner, Dries van Jaarsveldt, had lived there for a while, writing poetry. But he had soon lost interest and left for Johannesburg where, he said, he could make more money selling stocks and shares than writing for people who had no appreciation of the deeper meaning of life.

'Daleen,' he had asked her, 'Doesn't this say *anything* to you?'

> 'In the deepest ocean of my heart
> there pounds a raging turbulence
> which ebbs and flows
> and swells and crashes
> onto the pain of secret rocks …'

'*AG*, NO MAN STOP! Sorry Dries, but it says absolutely nothing. Rather try stocks and shares. I'll take care of your cottage, don't worry.'

So Dries's cottage would take care of Olympia's accommodation needs and, as for Olympia's other problem, Daleen knew this could not be as easily solved and she would have to enlist the help of the women. She'd tackle that one tomorrow. Right now her head was swimming, Olympia was nodding off, and they both needed to get some sleep. But before going to bed, she wrote to Dries that his little place had gone at last, but that she could get him very little rent for it and he should be grateful for anything, because who else would want a shoebox.

Olympia put her suitcases down on the doorstep of Number Six, and for the first time Daleen saw her smile.

'Will it do?' Daleen asked anxiously. 'I know it's small, but it does have a nice big garden. Look! there are two enormous fig trees – purple and green figs, both – and a lemon and an orange and even a grapevine on the pergola over there. There's lots of room to grow vegetables, and at least there are a few pieces of furniture inside – a couple of beds and a nice rocking chair and a lovely big table in the kitchen.'

Olympia was speechless. Daleen thought she was going to cry again, and in fact she did, but it was from gratitude rather than disappointment, shaking her head in amazement and joy until the little hairs on her chin quivered. 'Now you just stay here and settle down. I have to get to the office, but I'll be back in a while with some groceries.' And she left Olympia rocking herself gently in the old chair facing the garden.

On the way back to the office Daleen wondered what to do next. If she told Lily and Amelia, Maria and Sophia, Nellie and Anna, she knew that they would rush to call on Olympia, and so many rowdy women – well-meaning, but rowdy – could frighten the wits out of her. On the other hand, if she *did* tell them, she could count on their arriving with dozens of gifts, which would help to cheer Olympia up a bit. In the end, she decided that, rather than spread the news, she would tell only Lily, quietly and in detail. Lily could then explain the situation to the others, and then the six of them would know exactly what to do. They always did, these women of Corriebush. They always made a plan – and somehow, hit and miss as it often was, they invariably succeeded in putting things right.

So she asked Lily to come to her office, locked the door and unplugged the telephone. Then she seated her in the riempie armchair on the opposite side of her desk. 'Lily,' she began, 'I want you to listen carefully to this story, without interrupting. Then I want you to think hard before taking any action, like spreading the news. And finally, I want you to open your heart even more than you usually do. She needs us. You, me, all of us.'

'Certainly Daleen. If it's help that's needed, you know you can count on me. But how can I help if I don't know who I am helping?'

'Now there you go already. I said no questions.'

And then Daleen began the story, the strange, distressing story of the night before.

'There is a new lady in Corriebush. Old, but new. Just arrived.'

'Just arrived you say? That's funny. I was on my stoep most of yesterday with my jersey, and I didn't see anyone arriving. Perhaps she came just when I'd popped down to Sophia's to get some wool. I'd run out of the purple, you see. Did she come by taxi?'

'LILY!'

'*Ag,* sorry Daleen.'

'Olympia comes from Crete.' Lily opened her mouth but then quickly shut it again, and Daleen was able to carry on uninterrupted until the very end, until the church clock struck one. She waited for Lily to say 'Well! Lunch time!' But Lily simply sat there, dead still, saying nothing.

'So?'

Lily shook her head. 'I think, I think …' she mused. 'I think I must tell Herman.'

And off she went, slowly, thoughtfully, down the stairs, one by one, clipping and unclipping the catch on her handbag with each step. Not like Lily at all, thought Daleen, watching from above. She's really moved, Lily is.

Lily found Herman smoking his pipe on the stoep. 'I want to tell you about Olympia,' she said, 'and I want no interruptions.'

'I know all about Olympia,' he replied. 'Place in Greece. Pelopennese, to be exact. They used to worship there. One of their gods, I think it was Zeus.'

'Well I never,' said Lily. 'How did you know?'

'Daniel and I discuss these things, sometimes. I can tell you more. It was the scene of the Olympic Games. And they built a wonderful temple there.'

'Fancy that.' Lily was secretly impressed but wasn't going to show it, so she simply said, 'I told you not to interrupt and there you go already. Anyway, she's a woman, not a temple.'

Herman was undeterred. 'Not in *my* book, she isn't. But if *you* say Olympia is a woman that's fine with me, as long as you give her another name so that I know where I am. Why don't you call her Ollie?'

Lily did not reply, she simply gave an irritable flutter of her hand in Herman's direction and slowly, carefully started relaying every word she had heard that morning, starting with the moment Daleen had found Olympia on the pavement looking into the sunset.

'Olympia – Ollie to you – was born and bred in Crete. Crete is an island in the Mediterranean, south of the Greek mainland and …'

'Yes I know,' said Herman. Ignoring him, Lily continued.

'She and her husband, Dimitri, were peasant farmers. They owned – and still own, for that matter – a small piece of land in rural Crete, up in the mountains somewhere in the region of the Levká Óri. It was a hard life; they had to grow their own food and their only income came from the sale of sheep and cheese, and the fennel and basil that grows wild on the hills; but they were strong and able to work hard.

It took many years, however, before they decided that they could afford a family – Olympia was already well into her thirties. She gave birth to a daughter, and they called her Mali, short for Malia, where …'

'An ancient Minoan palace once stood.'

'That's right, Herman. A glorious palace. Sadly, Olympia could not have more children, but their Mali grew up quite shiningly lovely, and they showered her with everything they could possibly afford.

'In her turn, Mali rewarded them by growing into the prettiest girl in the village, her dark hair a tumble of curls, eyes that slanted up under black, arched brows, a smooth olive skin and a figure that grew as full and voluptuous as a ripe, dusky fruit. She was a loving daughter, who helped in the house and on the farm as much as she was able. And then, when she was seventeen, she told her parents that she was with babies.'

'*Ag*, no,' said Herman.

'*Ag*, yes,' said Lily.

'And what did Ollie and Dimitri say?' Herman was interrupting quite unashamedly now.

'They said 'Mali, and where did this foxtrot take place?'

She told them that it was in the lambing field, in the spring, when the hills were covered with wild flowers. At first they had just walked hand in hand, she said, admiring the different colours, but then the warmth of the sun and the song of the birds had made them a little dizzy with happiness and they had started to skip and dance, and then … and then … Mali had hung her head and asked for their blessing in marriage.

'Stefanos was a fine boy, they knew that. He and Mali had been friends ever since their school days. When his studies were completed, Stefanos had gone to work at a taverna in Paleochora, starting in the kitchen, but because of his startling good looks the owner had moved him up front, to entice and charm his customers. He was hard-working and had good prospects and so they were happy with Mali's choice, but when she told her parents of what he planned to do once they were married, they were horrified. Stefanos wanted to go to America. With a wife and family to support, he would need a good income, he said, and he believed he could earn really good money in a city, perhaps New York. He said they would leave the babies – Mali had a premonition they would be twins – with Olympia and Dimitri, their grandparents, and they would fetch them once they were settled in America and making a good living. Mali, however, did not think she could do it. 'Leave my babies? My *pethiá*? And you, *Mána*? And *Patéras*? It will break my heart.'

'My child, a wife's place is with her husband,' Olympia had replied. 'I will look after your babies until you come and fetch them. You must go with your man.'

They left their twins – a boy and a girl – with Olympia. It was a terrible parting, but Stefanos promised they would be back as soon as the time was right, and a weeping Mali said she would send money and a thousand letters. And then, it seemed, they simply vanished.

Five years passed. Five long years in which Olympia waited daily for news of Mali and Stefanos. She waited in vain. There was not a single letter. The endless anxiety during those years saw her visibly doubling in age, growing bent and wrinkled as she and Dimitri worked harder on the land than ever before in order to feed and clothe the twins. They were sturdy, happy children, but they needed plenty of milk and warm clothes in the winter. The seasons had been particularly bad, the market prices low, and they needed a new donkey; old Aesop could no longer manage the hills. What made everything worse was that Dimitri was not at all well. Previously so strong and energetic, he now looked exhausted and was losing weight, and finally Olympia persuaded him to see the village doctor. The prognosis was not good.

'It's his heart as well as his lungs, Olympia. He needs a dry climate and plenty of rest. You must get him away from rainy autumns, and off the land, or he won't last much longer.'

'But the children? What about the children? If we go away Mali will never find them! She hasn't sent her address, and I cannot write to her!'

'This is a small village, Olympia. Don't worry. When she comes back, I will be sure to know she has arrived. And I will tell her where to find her family. Now listen to me,' the doctor continued, 'this is my plan. You will take a ferry to Athens and leave the children there with my friend Carmela Iatrides, a good woman who has fostered many children. When you are settled, you can send for them.'

But where were they to go, Olympia had asked, trembling with fear and shock.

'You will board a ship – be sure to take the East Coast route – through the Red Sea and south to a seaport called Port Elizabeth. I have an old friend there, a Dr Marchant, whom I met at medical school in London. I will write and ask him to meet you and send you to the right place, where Dimitri will recover his health and where the twins can join you. Carmela will take good care of them, I assure you.'

When Olympia left the children, saw them waving to her from Carmela's doorstep, she distinctly heard her heart break.

'Olympia and Dimitri boarded the ship in the harbour at Piraeus. It was a long voyage, with bad food and violent storms. Dimitri did not make it beyond Mombasa, before collapsing completely. The ship's doctor ordered him to be put into isolation, no visitors, and strong medication, and he told Olympia not to worry. He would do his best, but the man was weak and strained, and anything could happen.

'It was then that Olympia's world simply broke apart. For the rest of the voyage she hardly slept or ate, expecting bad news every morning. But slowly Dimitri started responding to the rest and the medicine, and he was slightly improved when Dr Marchant met them at the quayside in Port Elizabeth. Nevertheless the doctor immediately arranged for Dimitri to go to hospital. He was tempted, he said, to put Olympia in as well, but she pleaded with him to let her go to where she was destined to be, else Mali would never find her if she was looking for her … no, she insisted on going to this place he called Corriebush, just in case, and please to send Dimitri as soon as he was better. In the meantime, she would make a living by doing embroidery. Dr Marchant called the taxi.

'And that,' concluded Lily, 'is the story I needed to tell you. Because I – and the other women – are going to have to put our heads together and work out a plan to get the twins here. And Mali, wherever *she* is. And Stefanos, hoping that *he* is where *she* is. And Dimitri too, if and when he makes it, poor chap. But where on earth do we start?'

For possibly the first time in her life Lily seemed defeated. This was so unusual that Herman knew he had to say something, and say it fast.

'You must call on her at once. Take food. Flowers. Anything. Ask her questions. Let her talk if she wants to. You talk if she doesn't want to. Take your friends along if you like, but you must tell them the whole story first, and insist that they remain reasonably calm and quiet.'

'You're right.' Lily gathered the others, told them about Olympia, warned them about her state, and not to be too loud or exuberant. 'They say a woman is like a teabag – you never know how strong she is until she hits the hot water – but remember this one has been through a lot.'

They understood perfectly. '*Ja*,' said Sophia. 'We must be careful. All our faces, suddenly at the door without warning. We must take it slowly.'

'Six at one go could be too much for anybody,' agreed Nellie.

'Might just tip the scales.'

Nevertheless, they banded together and paid their first visit the following afternoon.

Lily put her head round the kitchen door. 'Yoo-hoo, Ollie!' she warbled. Olympia was sitting in the rocker embroidering, but stood up immediately and, smiling shyly, waved them in while shuffling to the stove to put on the kettle.

'Herman says we must call you Ollie,' Lily bumbled on. 'It's a friendly little nickname you see. Nicknames are often given to a person if a person likes them.'

She knew she was messing it all up, but by this time Olympia was carrying a tray through to the table in the garden, and soon they had all gathered round with their baskets.

'Just a few little surprises,' Sophia said.

This was the start of many afternoon teas with Ollie. The women would chatter, and Ollie would sew. One by one, her tiny hands magicked fantastic fringed kerchiefs with colourful drifts of flowers, plump fruit, blue, blue seas, even dolphins – all the things that reminded her of her island.

'We must place orders,' they decided. 'It will keep her occupied, and we'll pay her well.'

Amelia ordered a striped skirt; Anna wanted an apron; Sophia said Dawid would look lovely in a bright waistcoat; and Lily thought Herman would like a crocheted cap.

Soon Ollie was making a good living and she enjoyed seeing her friends in her colourful creations but – although she never complained – she was far from settled or happy. Often, in the middle of one of their tea afternoons, her eyes would cloud over, and she would grow very quiet. It was almost as though she had left them for a while. At first they were disconcerted, not quite knowing how to handle her sadness. And then, on one such occasion, Nellie thought it might help if they allowed Ollie to reminisce.

'Ollie,' she said, breaking the silence, 'won't you tell us about your island home? We know very little about those parts, you know.'

And Ollie responded with such an eloquent rush, it quite astounded them.

'It – our little farm – lies somewhere in the hills between Paleochora and Chania, and quite a long way from Knossos.'

'Knossos?' they chorused.

'Knossos. You do not know about Knossos?' Ollie clucked her tongue. 'Knossos! King Minos, the palace, the gleaming palace with its grand stairways and priceless treasures! More than 5 000 years old and you haven't heard of it?'

They were mortified.

'Ah, perhaps because of the fires and the earthquakes,' Ollie continued. 'Not too much to be seen there now,' she added, wanting to comfort them. 'But in their day! Oh my goodness you won't believe how cultured the Minoans were. And so talented! Such beautiful pottery and jewellery! And royal apartments glowing with frescoes!' Ollie clapped her hands with excitement. 'The ladies were so beautiful in their flowing white dresses, and their men so handsome and strong – they could do a double somersault over huge bulls, you know, from front to back, while the women held onto the horns! And this all happened on *my* island – where the earliest, truly great civilization was born. It said so in Mali's book at school!' Ollie began to cry.

'Well, we did have our Voortrekkers,' put in Sophia, not wanting to be altogether outdone.

'Another time, another place Sophia.'

When they left, Ollie was visibly upset. All the talk about her island had brought back the pain of her missing family more sharply than ever, and the women realized that it was time to act.

'Something has to be done *now*. We can't leave our Ollie just sitting there with a broken heart and her embroidery. Hopefully Dimitri will soon be sent here, and the problem of him will, at least, be out of our hands – but her heart is aching for her child and her grand-children, and somehow we have to find them.'

'You know what I think?' said Amelia. 'I think one of us must go to Athens and collect the children from Mrs Iatrides – they're much too small to travel alone. They must be brought back here, and then I'll ask Daniel to make a plan with Mali. He knows people in high places. American authorities and so on.'

They all – every one of them – thought this was a splendid idea. The only problem was – who was to go? They all *offered* to go. It would, they said, be such an adventure; but secretly, they all found the idea terrifying. Not one of them had been further than Port Elizabeth, except for Nellie, who had been born in Johannesburg, but left when she was three.

'We should send two of us,' suggested Anna.

'Too expensive,' said Lily. 'After all, we will be paying the twins' fare as well.'

In the end they decided to draw matches. They broke two exactly in half. The third had a shorter tip and a longer end. They put them in Nellie's empty tea cup, closed their eyes, and dipped in.

'Oh my glory!' It was Sophia. Clasping her forehead with one hand, she waved the short match at the eager faces.

'It's me, and I'll *vrek*,' she said, white as a sheet.

'No you won't,' they told her quickly. 'You will love it, Sophia. Here's the chance to do the greatest act of kindness in your entire life. We'll arrange everything. Boat ticket, phrase book, papers for the government. You'll sail across the equator to Athens. Imagine Athens! The Acropolis! The Baklava! You'll be able to write a book when you come back!'

'Well, I've always wanted to see the Equator,' Sophia said, rallying somewhat. 'But you can forget the bull. I'm not a toreador, you know.'

'Now you're being stupid,' argued Amelia. 'Ollie was talking about 5 000 years ago. Daniel says Greece is one of the most interesting, civilized countries in the world. Now you start packing, and I'll ask him to start writing letters to people in high places.'

Feeling a little sick, Sophia went home to tell Dawid.

He met her at the gate. 'Have you heard?' he said, standing aside to let her through, noticing she was tottering slightly. 'Dimitri will be home tomorrow! Safe and sound, healthy and blooming; the hospital called Daleen to get Ollie's address.'

Sophia sank into the armchair on the stoep. 'Dimitri comes, I go,' she wailed.

'What are you talking about woman?'

Sophia told him of the plan and her short match.

Dawid was stunned but, not wanting to add to her concern, made light of the whole thing. '*Ag*, Sophiatjie, you'll have a lot of fun.'

The women decided a farewell party would be in order – a goodbye to Sophia and a welcome to Dimitri, who had arrived the previous week and who seemed, during his three-month stay in hospital, to have regained his former proud stature, powerful build and thick head of hair, just greying at the temples. He kept hugging little Ollie like a doll and then throwing her up above his head so that her skirt floated round her like a mushroom, and she would blush and slap him on the head. 'What a gorgeous man!' they said.

It was a merry party. They had all made little gifts for Sophia to pop into her suitcase, and although she was very quiet, for Sophia, there was a definite sparkle in her eyes. 'Got my papers and my passport,' she said, patting her big bag, 'and all I have to remember is to close my window at night.'

'Porthole, Sophia. You're not going on a train, remember.'

'I just hope the captain doesn't speed. Speed makes my head spin.'

It was just as they were seriously wondering whether Lily should rather go in place of Sophia, that there was a knock at the door. Dimitri jumped up, flung it wide, and let out a roar as in walked Mali, hugging a baby on her hip. Behind her came Stefanos carrying another baby on his shoulder, and behind them came the twins. The women burst into sobs, Dimitri broke into song, the twins leapt onto Ollie, and the babies started to cry.

For a long while no one spoke, there was simply just noise. And finally, when things had calmed down and Ollie – utterly speechless – had taken both babies on her lap, Dimitri spoke. It was while he lay in hospital that he, with the help of Dr Marchant and their village doctor, had been able to contact Carmela, who told them that Mali was already on her way.

Poor Mali. Stefanos had gone from job to job in New York. It had not been as easy as he had expected and Mali was dreadfully unhappy. But she had managed to get work in a laundromat, and had written to her parents every single week, slipping a dollar note or two into each envelope, and making sure that her reply address was clearly printed on the back.

But Mali never received a reply. She grew steadily more and more worried, and would have left Stefanos and gone back to Crete on her own to find out what had happened, but she had had another baby in America, and there was a fourth on the way. Had she known that the letters had never reached Olympia, much of her anguish would have been avoided. Looking back now, she realized her mistake. Thinking she was doing little Chuck Johnson, her landlady's son, a favour, she had made the mistake of handing the letters to him to post on his way to school, always slipping him a dime for his trouble. The minute he had rounded the corner, however, Chuck would slit the envelope, take out the money, and throw the letter into the nearest dustbin. She caught him in the act just before they were due to leave – for finally, after just under six years of hard work and scrimping, they had saved enough money for passage home for the four of them. The village doctor told Mali the whole story, as promised, and they wasted no time in boarding a ferry back to Athens to fetch the twins. Then they headed for the southern coast of Africa.

After the magnificent reunion, the entire family decided, without hesitation, to stay on in Corriebush. A profitable partnership developed between Dimitri and his son-in-law. Stephanos started a catering business, and Dimitri grew much of the produce for his dishes, working happily in the sunny garden in soil that was fertile and friable. Ollie continued with her little clothing business, Mali washed and cooked, the twins went to school and, because of all the happiness, there was a bit of foxtrot and nine months later, another baby. The house was extended, and every Friday night they had a party for all the good women of Corriebush and their husbands. There was a small Greek delicatessen in Port Elizabeth, and as long as they ordered in time, supplies were not a problem.

There was always lamb on the spit and hot bread and olive oil and dishes with names like Soutzoukákia and Afélia, Stifádo and Moussaka, along with salads and olives, slabs of feta cheese, and an abundance of wine and ouzo. When this took hold, the dancing started.

Mali and Stefanos and Ollie and Dimitri were on the tables in no time, and the others simply skipped from side to side, arms akimbo, wherever they could find a space, and when the plates started going – crashing onto the floor with shouts of laughter and more shots of ouzo – well then, it was *always* the signal for Sophia to remark that it was a bit of a *blerrie* waste.

'*Ag*, it's their way, Sophia. It's the ouzo that gets them so happy. You should try it.'

'No, I'll just stick to water thank you,' Sophia would reply, absent-mindedly sipping from the tiny glass filled with white liquid at her side. It never failed. In no time she was on the table too, having the time of her life.

'I was really looking forward to seeing the Equator and the Baklava,' she confessed later.

'Shame Sophia,' comforted Lily. 'But they're all here now, and going to stay.'

When the cottage became really too small for Ollie and Dimitri, Mali and Stefanos, the twins Yiorgi and Angelina, Yiannis and Grigor and Nikos, and they had managed to put away a nice pile in the bank, they bought the house next door, Number Seven, as well. It had a large garden to join up with Dimitri's, so he could double his output, and a flat roof, so they were able to build on a second storey. They painted both places snow white, with bright, bright Aegean blue roofs. The women presented them with a wooden plaque to nail on the front gate. They had all taken a turn at decorating the edges with posies of flowers, and in the centre, Nellie had carefully written the name in bold Gothic script:

Ollie's Place

Because that's exactly what it was.

OLYMPIA'S RECIPES

Greek food celebrates a heritage of natural assets: the sun, the soil, the sea, the rain – and the result is a fresh and natural cuisine that incorporates an abundance of vegetables and fruits, fish from their incredible blue waters, meat, wild herbs, honey ... To these, add coarse bread, salty white feta, and the stars of every Greek table – olives and olive oil – and there you have it. Simply outrageously delicious.

Olympia and her family never abandoned their culinary roots, and at their parties they took huge pleasure in introducing the flavours and memories of their homeland to their friends. Mali did most of the cooking, while Ollie bustled round tasting and advising. They loved to see the delight on the faces of their guests when they sampled the results, but it was the grand finale that was always Ollie's richest reward. Towards the end of the evening, when they were all full of good food and wine and warmth, when they had finished dancing and making merry, Herman would pick up his guitar, settle his chair under the fig tree, and start strumming. And Stefanos, washing dishes in the kitchen, would pick up the tune in a haunting song, a *madinatha*. His rich tenor voice would float out to the dark garden and the women would all start crying. This was always the moment that sent Ollie's universe spinning with joy. She would never be alone again.

OLLIE'S SUMMER PLATTER

Think roasted vegetables, anchovies and feta, salad leaves and green basil oil, and there it is – a brilliant salad that can be served either as a starter, or as a main course if you double up on the ingredients. Either way, it offers an eye-catching display. Use a really large platter and the vegetables almost dictate the arrangement themselves – salad leaves around the edge, wedges of feta in between, the roasted veg in the centre, the anchovies and olives patterning the top. The basil oil goes into a jug for sprinkling, and a crusty loaf goes somewhere. Despite the description, the whole picture takes little effort and no real expertise to prepare, and will surely be the star at a cold buffet.

2 brinjals (total 300 g), washed, halved and sliced into short fingers
200 g large brown mushrooms, halved
2 medium red peppers, seeded and cut into strips
8 pickling onions, peeled and halved vertically
30 ml (2 Tbsp) each olive oil and water
2 cloves garlic, crushed
2 ml (½ tsp) each dried oregano and sea salt
2 sprigs of fresh rosemary
200 g tomatoes, sliced into quarters and diced
mixed salad leaves and baby spinach, perhaps rocket if you have it
1 x 40 g can anchovied sardines, soaked in milk for 30 minutes
feta cheese, sliced into fingers
black olives (Costas Greek-style are good)

Place the brinjal slices in a colander, sprinkle with salt, and leave for about 30 minutes. Rinse and dry well. Arrange the mushrooms, red peppers and onions in a large baking dish. Mix the oil, water, garlic, oregano and salt together; mix into the vegetables and tuck in the rosemary. Roast at 200 °C for 30 minutes, or until the brinjal is cooked – the other vegetables will be ready. (The aroma is mouthwatering; open your kitchen windows while roasting, the neighbours will love you for it.) Remove from the oven, mix in the fresh tomatoes, discard the rosemary, then cool. Plate as suggested above – remembering that the drained anchovies criss-cross the veggies and the olives go in between – then stand back and look, and be very proud. **Serves about 4.**

To make the BASIL OIL whizz the following in a blender: a handful of fresh basil leaves; 125 ml (½ cup) olive oil; 60 ml (¼ cup) water; 10 ml (2 tsp) lemon juice; a pinch each of sea salt and sugar. It's difficult to estimate servings, it depends on the occasion, but if you have more than four diners, it's best to double up.

Roasted Fish with Herbs and Garlic Sauce

This is the recipe to use if your oven or baking dish can't cope with a whole big fish.
It requires just one side, filleted but skin on, head off, and weighing 900 g–1.1 kg.
Cape salmon is a fine choice. Slash the skin side, stuff with herbs, and roast on
a bed of onions, tomatoes and wine. The result is superbly succulent, with the
creamy garlic sauce the ultimate partner.

2 large onions, sliced into thin rings
45 ml (3 Tbsp) olive oil
3 large tomatoes, unskinned,
sliced into thin rounds
sea salt, milled black pepper, a little
sugar and dried oregano
125 ml (½ cup) white wine (to add later)
30 ml (2 Tbsp) fresh lemon juice, a few
slices of lemon, and butter

STUFFING
1 medium-thick slice crustless bread,
white or brown
about 8 fresh basil leaves
and 8 tufts of parsley
a few sprigs of fresh marjoram,
leaves only
a handful of snipped chives,
or spring onion tops
grated rind of ½ medium lemon
2 cloves garlic, chopped
a pinch of sea salt
15 ml (1 Tbsp) olive oil

Use a large baking dish to fit the fish flat, except for the extreme tail end – fold this under, so that the whole side is approximately the same thickness. Having checked this measurement, take the fish out again and set aside. Cover the base of the dish with the onion slices, drizzle with olive oil, top with the tomatoes, and sprinkle with seasoning, sugar and oregano. Bake at 200 °C for 25 minutes.

Meanwhile, make the stuffing by placing the bread, herbs, lemon rind and garlic in the bowl of a processor fitted with the metal blade. Blend well, then tip into a small bowl; add the salt and bind with the oil. Season the skinned side of the fish lightly, then turn over and make 6–7 deep diagonal slashes along the length. Gather up the stuffing and push it into the slits. Remove the baking dish with its juicy onion-tomato mixture from the oven, pour the wine over, then place the fish on top (skin side up). Drizzle with the lemon juice, arrange a row of lemon slices along the back, dot with a few pats of butter and bake for about 25 minutes or until cooked through. Serve from the dish, slicing between the slashes, and spooning over the soft onions, tomatoes and lovely juices. Serve with a green salad, hot, crusty bread, and the cold garlic sauce. **Serves 4–6.**

Greek-style garlic sauce

This is always served cold, even with hot foods, especially fried fish and brinjals.
It is also good with salads, and as a dip for raw vegetables.

1 large potato

2–3 cloves garlic, crushed

90 ml (6 Tbsp) olive oil or half olive
and half vegetable oil

30 ml (2 Tbsp) white wine vinegar
(I use white balsamic)

45 ml (3 Tbsp) ground almonds

30 ml (2 Tbsp) water

a little sea salt

Boil the potato, then peel and mash – do not add any liquid. Measure by pressing firmly into a measuring cup – you should have 125 ml (½ cup). Spoon into the bowl of a processor fitted with the metal blade, along with all the other ingredients. Process until the mixture becomes white and smooth; check, and add another pinch of salt if necessary, spoon into a small glass bowl and refrigerate, covered, for 3–4 hours to allow the flavours to mellow before serving a small dollop with each portion of fish.

PILAFF WITH MUSHROOMS AND GARLIC PRAWNS

A pilaff can be a simple side dish of rice cooked in stock, or fattened up as a main dish
by adding meat, veg or poultry. This recipe features prawns as the extra ingredient,
and because they don't come cheap, the pilaff is padded out with mushrooms and tomatoes,
with the garlicky, buttery prawns and a crumble of feta coming in at the end.
The result, in about 30 minutes flat, is a pink, succulent pilaff ready to
be ladled into deep bowls for individual servings.

150 ml (⅗ cup) tomato purée
300 ml (1⅕ cups) fish stock (chicken is definitely second best here)
30 ml (2 Tbsp) olive oil
1 medium onion, finely chopped
250 g button mushrooms, wiped and sliced
250 ml (1 cup) uncooked white long-grain rice, rinsed and drained
2 medium tomatoes, skinned and chopped
60 ml (¼ cup) white wine
2 bay leaves
5 ml (1 tsp) each sea salt and sugar
15 ml (1 Tbsp) olive oil
30 ml (2 Tbsp) butter
300 g (or more) shelled, deveined, defrosted prawns*
3–4 cloves garlic, crushed
a squeeze of fresh lemon juice
90–100 g feta cheese, cubed
a few fresh basil leaves, torn

Heat the tomato purée with the stock, then set aside. Heat the oil in a wide, deep saucepan, and add the onion and mushrooms. Toss over a low heat until softening, then add the rice. Stir until coated, then add the hot liquid, tomatoes, wine, bay leaves, seasoning and sugar. Bring to the boil, then cover and simmer over very low heat until the rice is tender and the liquid absorbed – about 25 minutes. Meanwhile, heat the second quantity of oil and butter in a frying pan and add the prawns. Toss until pink, curled, opaque and cooked through – this does not take long. Towards the end of the cooking period, crush in the garlic, and sprinkle in the lemon juice. Tip the whole lot into the cooked pilaff, and fork in the feta and basil. Remove from the heat, cover, and stand for 5 minutes. Remove the bay leaves, check seasoning, and serve. **Serves 4–5.**

* If using a larger quantity of prawns, add
a little extra butter/oil when cooking.

Quick Chicken Oregano

Marinate it, bake it, and out comes chicken with loads of flavour.
This incredibly simple dish requires minimal effort and only a few ingredients,
yet it's always relished and a treasure for the busy cook. You could use chicken pieces,
as in a braai pack, but thighs are the best for succulence, and they'll all cook through
at the same time. Serve hot with a platter of roasted vegetables and yoghurt,
or at room temperature with a Greek salad for a patio picnic.

8 chicken thighs (about 1 kg),
trimmed of excess fat
60 ml (¼ cup) olive oil
3–4 cloves garlic, crushed
15 ml (1 Tbsp) dried oregano
60 ml (¼ cup) dry white wine
1 ml (¼ tsp) ground cinnamon
10 ml (2 tsp) runny honey
sea salt and milled black pepper

Make two slashes on the skin side of each thigh. Mix together the remaining ingredients, except the salt and pepper, in a shallow baking dish; add the chicken, skin side down, and refrigerate for 2–3 hours, turning once. Place the thighs on the oiled rack of a grill pan, skin side up, pour the marinade over, and then season each piece. Add a little hot water to the grill pan to prevent scorching and to keep the chicken moist, then bake at 180 °C for 50–60 minutes, or until well browned and cooked through, adding extra hot water to the pan whenever necessary. It is important to keep the liquid topped up, in order to provide succulent juices to pour over the cooked thighs. Arrange on a warmed serving platter, pour pan juices over, and serve. **Serves 4–6.**

CHICKEN WITH RED WINE, FIGS AND WALNUTS

The gorgeous depth of colour and explosion of spicy flavours make
this chicken dish quite different from any other. It really is most unusual,
and deeply delicious served with a Greek salad without the feta, and a grain,
or orzo (small barley-shaped pasta).

8 large chicken thighs (about 1.2 kg)

30 ml (2 Tbsp) flour

7 ml (1½ tsp) dried oregano

5 ml (1 tsp) sea salt

30 ml (2 Tbsp) olive oil

1 large onion, finely chopped

5 ml (1 tsp) each ground cinnamon
and coriander

1 ml (¼ tsp) ground allspice (pimento)

300 ml (1⅕ cups) seasoned
chicken stock

125 ml (½ cup) red wine (a mature
claret is a good choice)

2 bay leaves

6–8 (about 130 g) ready-to-eat,
soft dried figs, quartered

coarsely grated rind of 1 lemon
(use a zester if possible)

coarsely chopped walnuts and
chopped parsley for topping

Remove the skin from the thighs – just pull, it's quick, and easier than finding skinless thighs in a supermarket. Once skinned, weigh – you should have 1 kg. Mix the flour, oregano and salt. Make 2–3 slashes on the skinned side of each thigh, and rub with the flour mixture (do the reverse side as well, although it's too bony to slash). Heat the oil in a large frying pan and brown the thighs lightly on both sides – do this in batches and then arrange in a baking dish, skinned side down, and quite closely together, but with space for the generous sauce. Add the onion to the frying pan and, if necessary, a dash more oil. Add the spices. Toss over a low heat and, when fabulously aromatic, add the stock, wine and bay leaves. Bring to the boil, pour over the chicken, cover securely with a sheet of greaseproof (not waxed) paper, and then a lid or foil. Bake at 160 °C for 1 hour. Turn the pieces, mix in the figs and lemon rind, and bake, uncovered, for a further 30 minutes; the sauce should be dark and fairly thick, the chicken tender and succulent. Check the seasoning – it may need salt and perhaps a squeeze of fresh lemon juice. Sprinkle with the topping, return to the oven for just 5 minutes, then serve. **Serves 6–8.**

Chicken and Aubergine Casserole with Herbs

If you love Greek-style ingredients, this one is for you – a dish of
saucy chicken and vegetables, with a topping of fresh herbs and pine nuts.
You need only a smattering, but even then they are expensive, and feta cheese
can be substituted very successfully. Once assembled, the dish is oven-baked,
where it all comes together with little further attention from the cook.

olive oil

1 kg chicken thighs,
trimmed of excess fat

1 large onion, finely chopped

400 g aubergines (brinjals), washed,
cubed, dégorged and patted dry

4 cloves garlic, chopped

400 g tomatoes, skinned and chopped

45 ml (3 Tbsp) flour

375 ml (1½ cups) hot chicken stock

15–30 ml (1–2 Tbsp) honey

2 sprigs of fresh rosemary

30 ml (2 Tbsp) brandy

a little sea salt

125 ml (½ cup) chopped mixed herbs*

a scattering of lightly toasted pine
nuts, or 100 g feta cheese, crumbled

* Use a mixture of chopped parsley,
mint and oregano in the ratio of
half parsley and quarter each
mint and oregano.

Brush a frying pan with a little olive oil. Add the chicken, skin side down, and brown well, then turn and lightly brown the other side. Remove to a baking dish, large and deep enough to take the chunky sauce, arranging the chicken skin side down. Add the onion, aubergines, garlic and tomatoes to the pan, adding a splash of water if the drippings have disappeared. Stir over low heat until just softening, then sprinkle in the flour and, when absorbed, stir in the stock, honey, rosemary, brandy and salt. Pour over the chicken – it will disappear completely under the sauce – then cover with a lid, or a sheet of greaseproof paper and then a sheet of foil. Bake at 180 °C for 15 minutes, then reduce the heat to 160 °C and bake for a further 45 minutes. Turn the thighs right-side up and bake, uncovered, for 30 minutes more until tender, and the sauce is bright, thick and bubbly. Sprinkle with the herbs and then with the nuts or feta, and return to the oven, still uncovered, for 10 minutes. **Serves 6.**

Saucy Lamb Knuckles with Butternut and Chickpeas

These are the tenderest knuckles, slow-baked in a sauce plumped with
unusual ingredients and spicy flavours. The dish is quite different from a bredie,
and makes the most of a modest amount of lamb. A side dish of braised brinjals
and peppers would round it off nicely, or simply a good spinach salad and brown rice,
or baby potatoes. A dollop of Greek yoghurt on the side is an indulgent but super option.

950 g–1 kg free-range Karoo
lamb knuckles, sliced

oil

sea salt to taste

2 medium onions, finely chopped

3–4 cloves garlic, crushed

10 ml (2 tsp) each ground cumin
and coriander

30 ml (2 Tbsp) flour

250 ml (1 cup) hot, seasoned
beef stock

125 ml (½ cup) red wine

1 x 410 g can chopped, peeled
tomatoes (as opposed to whole
peeled tomatoes, if possible)

15 ml (1 Tbsp) tomato paste

1 medium butternut, peeled and diced
(400 g prepared weight)

15 ml (1 Tbsp) honey

2 fat sticks cinnamon

4 bay leaves

1 x 410 g can chickpeas,
drained and rinsed

coriander leaves for topping

Heat a little oil in a large frying pan and brown the
lamb well on both sides. Remove to a large, deep
baking dish – the knuckles should not be crowded
as the sauce is bulky – a 30 x 24 x 6 cm dish is
dead right. Season the knuckles. Add the onions,
garlic and spices to the pan drippings, toss for
1–2 minutes (if dry, add a dash of water rather
than more oil), then add the flour, stir until
absorbed, then slowly stir in the stock, wine
and tomatoes. When thickening, add the
remaining ingredients, except the chickpeas.
Bring to the boil, then mix into the lamb. Push
the bay leaves and cinnamon right in. Cover with
a lid, or greaseproof paper and then foil, and bake
at 160 °C for 1¼ hours. Remove the bay leaves
and cinnamon. Add the chickpeas, cover again
and bake for a further 30 minutes, by which time
the lamb should be softly tender and the sauce
thick and plentiful. Sprinkle with coriander leaves.
Serves 5–6.

LEG OF LAMB, SLOW-BAKED WITH HERBS

Greek-style lamb: very well-done, very tender, robustly flavoured, richly browned –
and baked uncovered. This method of cooking combines roasting and braising.
The lamb nestles in fragrant, gently simmering juices, the house is filled with
the aroma of herbs and wine, and although it's not quick, it's not tricky either.

1 x 2 kg leg free-range lamb,
trimmed of any blobs of fat

vinegar

4 cloves garlic, slivered

100 ml (⅖ cup) fresh lemon juice

60 ml (¼ cup) olive oil

12.5 ml (2½ tsp) dried oregano

a few grinds of black pepper

a *small* pinch of ground cinnamon

3 sprigs of fresh rosemary

1 medium onion, sliced into thin rings

2 bay leaves

sea salt

250 ml (1 cup) hot water

125 ml (½ cup) red wine

Using a sharp knife, remove the outer membrane
from the lamb, wipe with vinegar, and push the
garlic into slits all over. Mix the lemon juice, oil,
oregano, pepper and cinnamon in a baking dish a
little larger than the leg, and deep enough to take
the liquid later on. Use a baking dish not a roaster,
which could react with the lemon and wine. Roll
the lamb over and over in this mixture until well
coated, then marinate overnight in the refrigerator,
turning in the morning. Before starting to cook,
return the lamb to room temperature and turn best
side up. Slip the rosemary, onion and bay leaves
underneath, and roast at 200 °C for 20 minutes.
Remove from the oven. Salt the top lightly, pour in
first the hot water and then the wine. Reduce oven
heat to 160 °C and leave the lamb in it for 2 hours.
Turn, salt this side very lightly, and bake for a
further 1½ hours. The juices should only just shiver
and pop throughout, and if your dish is the right
size you should not have to add any liquid, but
baste occasionally. When the time's up, the leg
burnished, and the 'gravy' a deep brown, remove
to an ovenproof serving dish. Use a paper towel
to skim the fat from the juices, strain, and spoon
some over the lamb. Turn the oven down to 110 °C
and let it rest there (loosely covered, with damp
greaseproof paper) for 15 minutes before carving.
Serve remaining gravy separately. **Serves 6.**

Vegetable and Chickpea Stew with Olive Bread

A favourite vegetarian dish of slow-simmered vegetables in a sauce spiked
with cinnamon and topped with cheese – so easy, anyone can make it,
and the bread is not complicated either – plump and studded with black olives,
it looks fabulous, and adds great personality to the homespun stew.

60 ml (¼ cup) olive oil

1 large onion, halved and sliced into crescents

2 x 200 g aubergines (brinjals), cut into chunks and dégorged

2 sticks table celery, thinly sliced

2 cloves garlic, crushed

500 g ripe tomatoes (not canned), skinned and chopped

2 ml (½ tsp) ground cinnamon

1 fat stick cinnamon

10 ml (2 tsp) tomato paste

10 ml (2 tsp) honey

250 ml (1 cup) vegetable stock or water

1 x 410 g can chickpeas, rinsed and drained

a little sea salt to taste

lots of crumbled feta cheese for topping

Heat the oil in a large saucepan. Add the onion and, when soft and golden, add the aubergines. Toss around to coat the chunks with the oil, then add the celery, garlic, tomatoes, cinnamon, tomato paste, honey and stock. Mix, then cover and simmer *very* gently for 30 minutes, stirring now and then to mash up the tomatoes. Add the chickpeas and a little extra stock or water if you think it necessary, then continue simmering for a further 15–20 minutes, until the vegetables are softly mingled, and the sauce thickened. Check the seasoning, remove the cinnamon stick, sprinkle with feta and serve when heated through – or serve as is, and pass the feta separately.

Serves 4, and is easily doubled.

Olive bread with pine nuts and garlic

This super, savoury bread is really easy to make – mixed in minutes,
the batter is plopped into a cake tin, smoothed out, left to rise, then baked –
and out comes a plump round bread, studded with black olives and aromatic things.
As it's a no-knead bread the texture will be dense and holey, but it nevertheless slices easily,
right across, into long thin slabs, or it can simply be broken into chunks.
Serve fresh and warm – or reheat for about 10 minutes in a moderate oven.

4 x 250 ml (4 cups) white bread flour

7 ml (1½ tsp) sea salt

15 ml (1 Tbsp) honey

15 ml (1 Tbsp) instant dry yeast

4 fat cloves garlic, crushed

a small handful of chopped curly
or flat-leaf parsley

2 pickling onions, coarsely grated

100 g calamata olives (drained
weight), rinsed, pitted and halved

30 ml (2 Tbsp) olive oil

45–60 ml (3–4 Tbsp) pine nuts

about 375 ml (1½ cups) very warm
but not *hot-hot* water

2 fresh sprigs of rosemary and
a few pine nuts for topping

*** If using a spring-form tin, put a tray
underneath in case of oil drips.**

Mix all the ingredients, except the water, in a large mixing bowl. Slowly add 250 ml (1 cup) of the water and mix in. The batter will still be a little dry. Add the rest of the water and, stirring briskly with a wooden spoon, mix to a soft and sticky batter, rather like chewing gum. You might need an extra 5–10 ml (1–2 tsp) of water to make it sloppy enough without being wet. Have ready a round cake tin*, 22 x 7 cm, first lightly oiled and then lined, base and sides, with baking paper. Scoop the batter into the tin and spread it out, repeatedly, with the back of a dampened spoon – stroke it right out to the sides, as evenly as possible. Press the rosemary and pine nuts lightly into the top, cover with a cloth and leave to rise for about 1 hour, until the batter has risen almost to the top of the tin. (Instant yeast is usually very quick, but this batter is heavy due to the olives, and therefore takes longer than usual.) When puffed up and ready, bake on the middle shelf of the oven at 200 °C for 20 minutes, then reduce the heat to 180 °C and bake for 20 minutes more – it should be nicely browned. Stand for about 10 minutes, run a spatula round the sides, then turn out onto a rack, remove paper, and tap the bottom – if it sounds hollow, you can be sure your bread is done.

Chilled Spanspek in Syrup

A long bath in a syrup of orange juice, honey, cinnamon and brandy
works magic with melon, and creates the perfect dessert after a hearty meal.
In Greece, eating fresh fruit at the end of a meal is the regular thing;
sweets and pastries are enjoyed at other times, with coffee.
Admittedly, this spanspek is not absolutely fresh and pure,
but it's refreshing, truly delicious, and incorporates Greek-style ingredients.
Make it up to 24 hours in advance and preferably serve it neat,
without Greek yoghurt or ice cream, unless pushed.

1 large, ripe spanspek (sweet melon)
250 ml (1 cup) fresh orange juice
2 ml (½ tsp) ground cinnamon*
45 ml (3 Tbsp) pale honey,
e.g. fynbos or veldflower
30 ml (2 Tbsp) brandy

* This will not 'melt' – the tiny specks
will float around in the syrup and
it matters not. It's the flavour that
is important.

Halve the spanspek vertically, cut into quarters, peel and seed, then weigh the flesh – you will need about 650 g. Slice each quarter into sickle-shaped segments, and halve each segment again so that you have a pile of neat, almost new-moon shapes. This is much better than dicing or balling the flesh, as there's no wastage, and it's quicker and neater. Pack the slices tightly together in a fairly large, deep dish. Mix the remaining ingredients in a small saucepan and heat gently, stirring, until the honey has dissolved – just lukewarm, really. Pour this syrup over the slices and refrigerate, covered, for at least 6 hours, but preferably overnight. Spoon the syrup over each serving. **Serves 5–6.**

RICE PUDDING

The Greeks love rice pudding and so do millions of others,
except possibly children at boarding school. Because it is not oven-baked
(which is probably the nostalgic rice pud most people remember), but prepared
on the stove (which is a quicker method for their Rizógalo), it does require a session
of stirring. It also requires a *very* deep saucepan because boiling milk froths up like a plume –
but it takes only about 30 minutes to produce four creamy, golden, sweet endings to a meal.
Concerning the rice – long-grain is sometimes used, but it just isn't the same as short,
plump pudding rice – which is difficult to find in this country and so I have taken a liberty
and substituted arborio (or risotto rice). It works like a dream.

125 ml (½ cup) water
80 ml (⅓ cup) arborio rice
a large pinch of sea salt
800 ml (3⅕ cups) full-cream milk
60 ml (¼ cup) castor sugar
1 large free-range egg
7 ml (1½ tsp) cornflour
extra 60 ml (¼ cup) milk
2 ml (½ tsp) vanilla essence
ground cinnamon for topping

Rub the base and right around the rim of a deep, heavy-based saucepan with soft butter – this will help prevent sticking and stop the milk from boiling over. Bring the water to the boil. Add the rice, give it a stir and, when the water is absorbed, add the salt and, slowly, the milk and sugar, stirring all the time. When it comes to the boil, reduce the heat immediately and simmer gently for about 30 minutes, or until the rice is very soft. Bear in mind that once the milk has calmed down and the mixture is just bubbling softly, there is no need to keep stirring; however, do not go away, as it does need occasional stirring throughout the cooking period, to prevent sticking. Beat the egg, cornflour and extra milk together, pour in a little of the hot milk mixture, stir to mix, then return to the saucepan and stir over low heat for about 5 minutes until thick, yellow and creamy and the egg is cooked, like custard. Stir in the vanilla essence, then pour or spoon into four heatproof bowls or glasses, sprinkle with cinnamon, and leave to cool. Best served at room temperature, otherwise refrigerate once cooled. **Serves 4.**

SYLVIA

Behind the gate of Number Two stood a square house with blue walls, yellow shutters and a pink front door. On either side of the front steps, two large, green-painted paraffin tins spilled over with ferns and trailing geraniums, and the path leading down to the gate was a cobbled meander of grey river stones, tufted with thyme and flanked with nasturtiums. It was altogether an unusually bright little place, and Big Joe and his son Jolly kept it as neat as a pin. Every morning, Jolly shook out the bedding and swept the front path, and every evening before leaving for work, Big Joe drew the lace curtains and placed lighted candles in the two windows.

'We don't expect her to come back,' he told Jolly. 'But one never can tell.'

Big Joe's wife had run off one day with a man who regularly visited Corriebush, selling insurance. Big Joe had never given a thought to the idea that there might be a little bit of foxtrot going on between the insurance man and his wife, so when she went off with him it was an awful shock. They had always been very happy together, the three of them, or so he had thought. Of course, Sylvia was a good deal younger than he was – only nineteen when he had married her – and the women of Corriebush had warned him to think about it very seriously, but he was enchanted by her shy charm and youthful beauty; he really loved her, believed she loved him, *and* he was lonely, so whatever they said made absolutely no difference. Now he clearly recalled their words.

'It's not that we're interfering, Big Joe,' Anna had told him gently, 'but we all care so much about you, and we hardly know Sylvia. She's still so young, and we're worried that if the marriage doesn't work out, it will bring even more unhappiness into your life.'

Maria was more forthright. 'She's just looking for a man to get her off the farm,' she told him. 'It can't be much fun for her, living on that place in the mountains with those old parents of hers. But why must she choose you, Big Joe? I don't like it, don't like it at all.'

'She's after an older man to spoil her with pretty things,' Lily warned. 'She'll go through your salary like a knife through butter, just you watch.'

'Big Joe,' they had told him, one after the other. 'You're such a good man, you deserve only the best. A worthy woman with a heart of gold and never mind the pretty face. You've waited a long time since your wife passed on, you can wait a bit longer for the right one to arrive, can't you? After all, you hardly know the young girl. And what about Jolly?'

Jolly was not like other children. He was no trouble at all, but he had a twisted leg and had never learnt to speak. His birth had been a difficult one, and Big Joe's wife had died within a few days, after complications set in. That was ten years ago. Ten lonely years for Big Joe, and now at last he'd found Sylvia, and the women were causing a hell of a fuss.

'I'll tell you straight,' it was Maria again. 'I think it's your looks. When you first arrived in Corriebush I said to Anna, "Anna," I said, "I think Hollywood has come to town. Gary Cooper himself, with those crinkly eyes and long legs and the square jaw and shy smile." In my opinion, she's just got a crush on you because you're handsome, and crushes never last, you know. Like falling stars. Here today, gone tomorrow.'

Big Joe had listened politely to all their dark warnings. He never argued, never contradicted. He just smilingly ignored them and went on his way, happy in the knowledge that for once he held a secret unbeknown to the well-meaning Corriebush women. It was this. Sylvia was no stranger to him. He had already known her for over five years, watched her mature and grow ever more beautiful, and was as sure of his love for her, and hers for him, as he was sure the sun would rise in the morning.

Sylvia was still a schoolgirl at the time of their first meeting one stormy April morning. He had been trimming the quince hedge that grew on the boundary of his garden, when he heard a thump on the pavement and a girl cry out in pain. Hurrying out, he had found Sylvia sitting clutching her knees, which were streaming blood, staining her white socks and trickling over her lace-up shoes, making little wet brown patches on the stony ground. She was crying and he picked her up and carried her into the house, sat her on a chair, and set about cleaning up the mess. He knew exactly what to do. He had done the same thing often, with Jolly. The water, the disinfectant, the Mercurochrome, the ointment, the plaster, it was all done in minutes, and by the time she had drunk a cup of sugar-water, she was laughing.

'What happened?' Big Joe asked. 'And what are you doing out of school in the middle of the morning?'

'I'll tell you in a minute,' she said. 'But first let me thank you.'

And she gave him a smacking, childish kiss on his cheek.

'It was in biology. Halfway through the lesson the teacher said "Oh dash it. I've left the experiment at home. Frog in a jar. Sylvia, *liefie*, run and fetch it for me – you know where I live, just ask my husband to give it to you. And hurry, I must have it before the bell rings."'

Sylvia stopped and smiled. 'I know your name is Big Joe. Everyone knows you, because … well, just because. And so, Big Joe, when the teacher said "Go", I jumped. When you're a boarder in a hostel you just love getting out of those gates. But once outside, I couldn't run. I mean, it was such a lovely damp morning and I felt so free, walking slowly past the reservoir with the ducks, past the sign that reads – This Way To The Corriebush Mountain Path. Swinging on the Monkey Ropes Strictly Forbidden. Beware of Snakes. You know, that one?'

Big Joe nodded.

'And then when I came past your house, I was looking up at the sky. There was this strange light that sometimes happens before a storm, it's like an egg scrambled with too much milk – that colour – and you know there's going to be a thunderstorm. I love it when it's all over, and the birds start singing as though it's early morning.'

'And then you fell.'

'And then I fell, and you fixed me up, and I'm going to be *very late* with that frog!' And Sylvia jumped up, winced a little, then kissed him on the other cheek. 'I'll bring you some of Mam's fig jam when next she comes to town.' And she did.

After that Sylvia often dropped in, and Big Joe found himself really looking forward to her visits. They would have tea together, while she shared her scones with Jolly and chattered about school and exams. And then suddenly – it happened in one afternoon – Big Joe became aware that this girl was no longer the bouncy schoolchild he had first met. She was nearly seventeen, her school days were coming to an end, and Sylvia was on the brink of becoming a mature, serene and very lovely young woman. She still chattered about exams, her life on the farm and her hopes for the future, but at times she would fall silent and just look at him with those wide, honest blue eyes and he knew, knew even then, that in time this warm, sensual spark that was beginning to fly and flick between them would flare up and grow, and he knew that she knew it too.

But Sylvia's parents had plans for their bright daughter.

'The child must be qualified for something,' they decided. 'Can't have her sitting here on the farm waiting for a man.'

So they sent her to the Technical College in Bloemfontein to take a secretarial course, and for a full year Big Joe did not see her.

And then one day he met her in town. Eighteen years old now, the course completed, and she was back on the farm for the December holidays. They were standing at the cake stall at the church bazaar, and she handed him a fairy cake she had just bought.

'I've missed you,' he said.

Sylvia gave him her open, frank look. 'And I've missed you,' she said.

Anna saw them. 'Now just look at that,' she nudged Maria. 'Standing staring at each other. He doesn't even see the cake. Something happening there if you ask me.'

Anna wasn't wrong, and it wasn't long before Big Joe had a long chat with the *dominee*.

'I don't know what to do,' he said, embarrassed. 'I see her and my heart just … my heart just stops. It's not her beauty. It's just Sylvia. I can't get her out of my mind, and the trouble is, she feels the same.'

He knew, because she had told him. The week after Christmas she had come to his house, just as she used to do, sat down at the kitchen table, passed him a biscuit and then taken his hand between hers.

'I love you Joe,' she said simply.

They agreed that her parents should be told immediately, before any plans could be made.

'But *liefie*,' her mother said, 'he might be the kindest, most handsome man in Corriebush, but for a girl of your age? This is a shock, a big shock. Wait a few years – at eighteen a girl often doesn't know her own mind.'

'I do know my own mind, Mam, and I want your and Pa's blessing. I have always done as you said. Studied hard. Gone to college. Never let you down in any way.'

They could not deny that she had never given them a moment's anxiety.

'I know he's twenty years older than me, but does that really matter?'

'Perhaps he won't ask you,' her father volunteered.

'He already has. And I don't think you can imagine how much I longed for him when I was at college. I thought of him all day and every day. I couldn't wait to finish and come back and then, when I did come back and go to town with you, I used to look for him all over – the Corner Shop, the butcher, I even used to walk past his house, up and down, and when I did see him I used to cry with happiness.'

'She's serious,' her mother said.

'Well, when did he propose then?' her father asked.

'At his front gate. I know it doesn't sound very romantic, but it was.'

They had gone to town – she and her parents – to do some shopping. Sylvia had gone off on her own and had met Joe just as he was leaving his house. They both lifted the latch of the gate at the same time and he had held onto her hand.

'Sylvie. When I see you my heart beats so loudly in my chest, I'm sure you can hear it and it embarrasses me.'

'Joe. Let me feel.'

And she slid her hand under his shirt – right there in the street, and said, 'Yes, I feel it. It's exactly the same as mine.'

And then the two of them just stood, because there was nothing more to be said, and they did not mind who passed, and who saw. It was done.

'He's going to ask your permission, Pa, as soon as you've got used to the idea.'

'I know his kind, salt of the earth,' was all her father said.

And her mother nodded, knowing this to be true.

Early in the New Year, the announcement appeared in the *Corriebush Chronicle* under 'Forthcoming Marriages'.

Big Joe offered to pay for the wedding reception, because he wanted to invite everyone in Corriebush. Naturally, they all accepted.

'We have to stick by Big Joe,' they said, 'even if we wonder a bit about the bride.'

'She's sure to look very pretty, though, with all that blonde hair and the white satin that Nellie is running up for her.'

'And at least he won't have to cook and clean anymore, so that will go a long way.'

'I just hope it's not his handsome looks that have gone to her head. I must say, though, if I were in her place, I would do the same thing, if you know what I mean.'

'No, Sophia, we don't know what you mean, but we hope she will prove us all wrong. The teachers tell me she was a shy girl at school. Never looked set for the city lights even with legs built to win a beauty competition. Very quiet, they said. The gentle kind.'

'And he's only twenty years older than she is, after all, and that's not too bad. Knows nothing about housekeeping of course, what with all that secretarial stuff. One doesn't need a typewriter to run a kitchen, but she's young enough to learn, and he can show her the ropes. Maybe we will all be nicely surprised.'

And certainly, in the beginning, nobody could point a finger at Sylvia for not caring for Big Joe and Jolly. She spent a lot of time in the kitchen, always had fresh flowers on the table, and made lace curtains for the windows. They knew, because they made it their business to keep an eye on the goings-on.

'We owe it to Big Joe,' they said. 'Don't really know the wife yet, but we can check on her when we pass, and when we're happy with what we see, we'll pay a call. It's not your regular marriage, remember, and we must let Big Joe know that he can always come to us if things aren't working out.'

Big Joe was astonished by their concern. 'Sylvia? *Ag,* she's the happiest woman in Corriebush! Always whistling. When I get home she's always there, whistling and singing and sweeping and baking, and sometimes she takes the broom and goes dancing all over the place. Always playing games with Jolly and always laughing, Sylvie is. She's happy alright.'

Only once did he admit to Sam that his salary as a blockman could hardly keep up with the monthly bills. 'But, after all, attractive young women like to buy pretty things, don't they? Dress up now and again and go shopping? Nothing wrong with that, is there?'

'Nothing wrong with that, Big Joe,' Sam agreed.

'And what if she does spend a bit too much on this and that? She brightens up the whole house with her talk. Full of chatter and jokes. Jolly and I can't think how it was without her.'

Big Joe really believed that Sylvia was every bit as contented as he was, so her running off like that came as a dreadfully cruel blow.

She did leave a farewell note, however, written on the back of an old Christmas card. It read: 'Sorry to do this, but I can't go on. Don't try to find me, I'll send money.'

And she did, in the beginning, but then suddenly it dried up.

'Perhaps she's gone to Wales,' the postman told Big Joe when he started waiting anxiously at the gate at the end of each month, hoping for a white envelope with a few pound notes enclosed. If Joe had not lost his job at the butchery, he and Jolly would have managed quite well. But Sam Smith, the butcher, decided to invest in some new, expensive machinery, which chopped and sliced and minced and completely took over Big Joe's work, and Sam simply could not afford to pay him and pay off the machinery as well.

At a meeting of the town councillors, Big Joe's plight was discussed. 'The people of Corriebush always stand together,' the mayor said. 'And we all know what has happened to Big Joe. His wife has run off. He has lost his job at the butchery. And he has a young child to support.'

They all understood that Jolly would never be able to contribute, could never help his father. 'I think we should make a job for Big Joe. The salary won't be much, but I suggest we appoint him as the town's nightwatchman.'

There was no crime in Corriebush, but that was beside the point, and they all agreed that it was a good idea.

Big Joe took to it at once. 'You never know,' he told Jolly. 'I might come across a robber one night and then I'll show him a thing or two.'

He set off at seven sharp each evening, and turned in when the sun rose. It was a long shift, but people were very kind. Almost every doorway cradled a packet of sandwiches or a flask of hot soup or a slice or two of cake, and he soon learnt to carry a small basket as well as his lantern, so that he could take some of the treats home for Jolly.

'Chocolate cake and meringues for breakfast today!' he would call, setting them out on the kitchen table. Or, 'Blow me down if it isn't half a roast chicken I've got here!' They would

have their morning meal together, and then Big Joe would check on the postman before going to bed. 'Time to turn in now,' he always said. 'Have to be on my toes tonight.'

'Of course I still miss Sylvie,' he told anyone who asked, giving no hint of his real distress. 'But I've fallen into the way of it now. And my job takes my mind off things.'

Big Joe never missed a single shift. Night after night his footsteps echoed down the lonely streets. He stopped at each house, lifted his lantern up high so that the golden glow rested on the front gates and garden paths, and then tilted it so that it swept the roofs.

'Shame,' they said, peeping from behind curtains. 'Best watchman a person could wish for.'

He soon came to know all the sounds of the night. Knew who was having to get up to a new baby. Who was making coffee at strange hours. Which couple was having an argument in the bedroom. 'Trouble brewing,' he would mutter.

Big Joe often shared things with Jolly.

'Boy, you should have seen the shooting stars last night! Falling like diamonds all over the place, just like Guy Fawkes!' Or 'There's a porcupine eating Hester's pumpkins, you know old Hester who lives near the church? I heard him snuffling away, shone my light and off he went, but I don't want to be there when she sees the holes this morning.' Or, 'Purple ring around the moon again, old man. Never a good sign, that.'

One night he passed Sam Smith's house just as Sam was latching his front gate. 'You sound happy, humming like that Big Joe!'

'Evening Sam. Yes, I hum when I walk. It's one of the songs Sylvie used to sing, you know.'

Sam put his hand on Big Joe's shoulder. 'I'm sorry, man. We're all really sorry and we're also a bit worried that you are not getting enough sleep. I mean, working all night, like this?'

Big Joe shrugged. 'It works just fine, Sam.'

He could sleep all day because he did not have to be concerned about Jolly. Unable to attend school, Jolly had always spent his days roaming the streets, perfectly safe and perfectly happy. Everybody knew him and was kind to him. People would slip him little treats, like lollipops and sherbert.

'Hello Jolly, where are you off to this morning?' And he would wave and give a crooked smile and lope off somewhere. Until the day Jolly 'died'.

Right in the heart of the town, near the Corner Shop, grew an enormous oak tree. They called the tree The Corriebush Times, because any news of local interest would be printed on a sheet of paper and pinned to the bark at eye level, where anyone passing would be sure to see it. Concerts and bazaars, horse shows and beetle drives, auction sales and rugby matches, all the exciting events, and then the sad ones too. A funeral notice was quickly spotted because it was printed inside a black border. And one morning, there was this awful thing: Jolly's death notice, and the time of the funeral that very afternoon. Jolly wasn't dead, but only the two schoolboys who had nailed up the fictitious announcement knew this. Everyone else read the notice, except for Big Joe. Being asleep, he knew nothing about it.

They all went to the funeral. The whole of Corriebush was there, standing in shocked and horrified huddles, the women in sombre black, the men in ties and suits, waiting for the hearse and the *dominee*. And then suddenly, from behind a tree, Jolly appeared.

The people froze, pale as ghosts, in a terrible silence. 'It was just like an eclipse,' Sam Smith's wife said later. 'You know, that sudden dark feeling that the world has come to an end. Not even a bird singing.'

Jolly smiled his lop-sided smile, gave a sort of wave, and then scrambled into the tree, dragging one leg slightly as he always did. Halfway up, he lay down flat on a branch and grinned at the gathering below him.

Nobody said a word. They simply stared up at him, open-mouthed. And then somebody started to sob and old Mrs Bruwer fainted outright, falling with a thump right where she stood. Men removed their hats. Mothers felt for their children, drew them into their skirts and covered their faces. It was only when Jolly slithered down into their midst that the dreadful thing happened.

The two boys who had pinned the notice on the tree shouted cruelly.

'Jolly! It's Jolly!'

'*Ai* no! Jolly's dead, man!'

'You're dead, Jolly! Go away Jolly!'

This sent the children running. They scattered in all directions, screaming 'Jolly! Jolly! It's a spook! A spook!'

And in utter confusion, their parents went after them. Only the *dominee* stayed and saw the shock, puzzlement and waves of despair that washed over Jolly's face. He had always known only love and acceptance. He had never encountered rejection. And he just stood there, devastated.

The next day, Jolly was found hanging from the same tree on which his death notice had been nailed, his braces caught up in a fork, twisted several times, his feet dangling way above the branch on which he must have stood before he slipped. He was still breathing shallowly, but his eyes were shut and he didn't move at all when they carried him down and to the hospital. Jolly was not expected to live, the doctor said, and the whole event became a total, hideous nightmare. The women wept, the men spoke of it in solemn whispers, and a hush fell on the town as though a grey blanket had dropped from the sky and stifled the life out of the place.

After one week, Jolly was still in a coma, and the doctor did not think he would ever come out of it.

'We can't send him home,' he told Big Joe. 'He needs round-the-clock nursing. We'll inform you if there's any change in his condition, but I don't hold out any hope, I'm afraid. None at all.'

The people took Big Joe cakes, and bunches of flowers from their gardens, and baskets of fruit and jugs of soup, and at night he walked the streets as usual, holding his paraffin lamp, shining it this way and that, down the main street, past the Corner Shop and round the park just as he always had done. Until the night he just kept on walking.

It was Harry the postman who raised the alarm early the next morning. At last he had a white envelope to deliver, and he was so excited that he sat smiling and tinkling his bicycle bell for a good few minutes before he realised that Big Joe was not at home. Harry peered through the windows and then opened the front door and called, to make sure, but Big Joe was definitely not there. So he put the envelope on the kitchen table, and raced off.

The news spread quickly and soon most of the men were out searching. They walked down every street and then out into the country, some even got into their cars and drove to a few farms and up one or two mountain tracks, and even a little way along the main road to Port Elizabeth, but he could not be found. 'It's as though the night just swallowed him up,' they said. 'The shock of it all has been too much.'

Worried and mystified, they talked of little else for days, and when Harry eventually went back and opened the letter, they were even more dismayed. It read: 'Sorry. Coming home. Love Sylvia.'

And she arrived exactly a week after Big Joe had disappeared. She looked much the same, a little thinner perhaps, and didn't explain her absence even though Maria from next door bustled over immediately the taxi drew up. Sylvia simply smiled at her, dumped her suitcase, and started to clean up the kitchen. And that's where Big Joe found her the day he came walking back. He just walked down the main street as though he had never been away, and round the corner to Number Two. The windows were open, the path was swept, the flowers blooming, and Sylvia was busy baking.

'You're back,' he said, tears running down his cheeks.

'I'm sorry,' she said, turning to put her arms round his neck. 'Oh Joseph, my sweet, dear Joseph, I am so, so sorry.'

It did not take long for the women to pay a call.

'We owe it to Big Joe,' Lily said. 'Find out what's going on with the young lady, then perhaps a person can help. I see he's walking at night again.'

'We'll visit her tomorrow afternoon,' they decided. 'No point in delaying tactics, as they say.'

And so they arrived: Anna, Sophia, Nellie, Maria, Amelia and Lily. It was a formidable gathering to find on one's doorstep, but Sylvia smilingly waved them in and offered tea.

Balancing her cup on the broad wooden arm of the chair, Nellie pursed her lips and fell to. 'As my friends know, I'm not one for beating about the bush, and so I'm going to ask you straight. What have you done with that insurance man? What was his name again?'

'Chrisjan. Chrisjan Terblanche.'

'That's the one. Terblanche. Good-looker with fair hair.'

'Chris. He's my first cousin from my mother's side. He picked me up.'

Six pairs of eyebrows shot up.

Sylvia helped herself to two spoons of sugar, and slowly stirred it into her tea, watching the spoon go round and round. Then she put her cup down without taking a sip, and looked at them squarely, each in turn, her blue eyes wide and steady.

'It was my cold,' she said. 'It all started with my cold.'

Encouraged now, they nodded. 'Your cold.'

'Perhaps that time of the month, too? We know how it is,' they went on, afraid she might stop. Sylvia ignored them and continued.

'I had a bad cold, so I went to see what I could find in the little medicine box in the bathroom. There were no cold pills there, but there was a small bottle of brandy, and I remembered my mother sometimes used to take brandy with lemon and honey and hot water when she felt poorly.'

'A fine old remedy,' Sophia agreed.

'So I drank some and I felt much better and very happy, but the next day I felt bad again, so I took a little more, but without the water this time. Again I felt better and very happy, and so I started having little sips all day because then I never felt lonely and I could dress up and go shopping and greet everyone, and I felt quite grand and not at all shy. And when the happy feeling stopped, I just took another dose. Anytime. Breakfast, lunch, supper, anytime. In the end I was using the grocery money to buy brandy from the bottle-store. I said I wanted it for bottling peaches.'

'"You're bottling a lot of peaches, Mrs Joe," Mr Daniels said to me.'

'"Yes, our trees are full," I lied to him. "Plums too, and apricots. You know how it goes, Mr Daniels, once the fruit starts one can hardly keep up and everything keeps so well if you put a little brandy in the syrup."'

Anna held up her hands. 'For goodness' sake child! Stop! You say you were lonely? How can anyone in Corriebush feel lonely? Everybody knows everybody here, we're all good friends, everyone's welcome, our hearts are big.'

'That's what you think, Auntie Anna. But when you're a new bride, married to a man whom everyone adores, and you're nineteen years old and have no idea how to entertain or dress for socials or lay on a really good tea party, then it becomes very lonely. The young people, those my age, have all gone to work in the cities. Oh yes, Auntie Anna, in Corriebush one can feel very lonely.'

The women were utterly shocked. 'We never thought …' but Sylvia was not to be stopped.

'It was like a torrent,' Anna remarked later. 'Poor girl, she must have suffered a lot to get it out like that.'

Sylvia rested her elbows on her knees, leaned forward slightly, and looked from one to the other as she spoke. 'You forget I went from boarding school straight to college. All I wanted, really, was to make a trousseau and get married and have children. I was never very clever at anything. But I really loved Joseph,' (she always called him Joseph now) 'and I tried my best to be happy in Corriebush. But you, Aunt Nellie, you and the other ladies, you made me feel really stupid and hopeless. I knew you were watching to see how I managed. I knew it was because of your fondness for Joseph, you wanted to make sure that he was happy and cared for. But what you didn't know is that you made me feel like an unloved, no-good child, who somehow managed to marry the most wonderful man in town. Like a fish in a bowl, like a monkey in a cage, I was being watched, and without saying a word, you were asking me to prove myself. I did not know how.'

Anna picked up her cup to take a sip and then forgot and put it down again.

'So I painted the house.'

They nodded, they had seen her with the blue paint and the yellow paint and the green paint and thought it all a bit wild, but had said nothing.

'That hurt. You said nothing. Then I made curtains.'

They nodded. They had noticed the little lacy things that hung skew and did not even cover the panes, and had said nothing.

'That hurt too. Then I planted flowers. And all you said, Aunt Nellie, was "Paraffin tins?" I had no money that month for pots. I spent it at Mr Daniels', as you now know.'

Thoughtfully and with great care, Nellie eased her skirt over her knees, over and over, until the hem hung to her ankles.

'On days when I felt especially hopeless, the tots grew stronger. By the time Joseph came home, my spirits had lifted, I was ready to sing and dance all over the place, I felt happy and light-hearted – and he never knew it was the brandy.'

'Oh my goodness. Oh my goodness! Sophia, your cake is on the floor.'

Sophia did not bother to pick it up, she just sat there, staring.

'Chris popped by regularly on his visits to Corriebush. He had always been my favourite cousin and we used to have lots of fun when he visited the farm. Here in town I never knew when he was coming, and so it did not take him long to catch me out.'

'"Sylvie," he said one day, "you've got one hell of a problem, girl."'

'"Problem? What problem?"'

'"You're drinking. I can see it – all the signs are there – your hands are shaking, and I can smell it, and it's only ten in the morning."'

'Well, I started to cry, and that was when it all came out. All of it – the way you all made me feel like a dunce and everything else. Chris promised not to tell Joseph, I was so ashamed, but he made me promise to return to Port Elizabeth with him.'

'"My parents will take care of you," he said. "They'll take you to doctors and meetings and do whatever is necessary to make you better. Pack your bags, Sylvie. You have to do this. For your sake, for Big Joe's sake, and for Jolly."'

'Because I loved them both, because I hated what I had done, and because I wanted to be strong, not weak, I went with him. And I could not tell Joseph why, because I was too ashamed.

'In the beginning, it was very hard for me, although my aunt and uncle were very kind, and Chris gave me money to send back to Joseph to make up for all the grocery money I had used on brandy. But then Chris lost his job and the money stopped.'

The sun was dipping behind the mountain that held Corriebush in its folds, and Sylvia said she should hurry up because she would soon have to wake Joseph for his night shift, and she had to visit Jolly in the hospital.

'Chris' parents kept me there until they knew, and I knew, that I was whole again. Now it is past.'

The teapot was cold and the slices of cake lay untouched. The women rose silently, full of thought. At the front door they shook Sylvia by the hand. When they got to the front gate they all turned back and enveloped her.

'We're so sorry, child,' they said. 'Seems we were all blind as bats, so concerned for Big Joe we clean forgot you needed caring too.'

They held her close, all six of them, and promised that from that day, that very minute, everything would be different. And they were true to their word.

The women of Corriebush adopted Sylvia. Not a day passed when one or the other didn't drop in for a chat. They invited her aged, hard-up parents to visit. They showed her off, introducing her to any newcomers as 'The prettiest, most capable young wife in Corriebush'. On her birthday they gave her two big urns for the garden, already planted with ivy. Aunt Nellie gave her free sewing lessons. And Sylvia blossomed into the beautiful, contented and loving person she was always meant to be.

The story of Number Two and Big Joe and Sylvia, with all its earlier sadnesses, ended happily. Big Joe was able to give up his job as nightwatchman when Sam Smith started a marketing and delivery service, and put him in charge of sales. Sylvia took up dressmaking and the orders simply flooded in.

The following year she gave birth to a baby boy, and they christened him Jo-Jo, because he was born on exactly the day Jolly was able to leave hospital and come home. Taller now, a lot stronger and steadier, he walked up the front path, smiled his crooked smile, and everything was right and just as it should be.

Sylvia's Recipes

Sylvia was not an accomplished cook, and in the beginning she served some rather extraordinary meals to Big Joe and Jolly. Because these were based on her experience of boarding school food, she tended to make much use of sago, pumpkin and canned pears. Big Joe never complained, he and Jolly ate everything she concocted, but Sylvie knew it was awful. So she started writing letters to her old schoolfriends, asking them for recipes and advice, and slowly she was able to put together a personal cookbook, and to work on her lack of skills. She was a determined young woman, and after her return to Corriebush and many, many months of ups and downs, flops and tears, she finally triumphed.

For Big Joe, every meal became a treat, for what Sylvia now served was comfort food at its best – totally unpretentious, pure and simple. He was so proud of her that he started inviting the women and their husbands round to supper. It was Servaas who eventually found the right words, and expressed what they all felt after having had a meal with Sylvie and Big Joe. Standing up, he proposed a carefully rehearsed toast. 'To Sylvia,' he beamed. 'A lady who, in her unassuming way, has polished the art of culinary simplicity to homespun perfection.'

'Ag, Servaas,' put in a bemused Maria. 'Why don't you just say it straight, man?' She raised her glass. 'To Sylvia, our clever young Cordon Blew. Cordon Blah. Bler. Ag, never mind. To Sylvie.'

Spicy Pumpkin Soup with Rooibos and Cream

A softly scented, softly golden, elusively flavoured soup with a flutter of spices and a little of South Africa's famous brew to add something special to the otherwise basic ingredients.

600 g firm-fleshed, bright orange pumpkin, peeled and diced (prepared weight)
2 medium carrots, sliced
1 medium sweet apple, peeled and chopped
1 medium potato, peeled and cubed
1 jumbo onion, chopped
2 ml (½ tsp) each paprika and ground ginger
1 whole clove*
1 fat stick cinnamon
500 ml (2 cups) chicken stock
sea salt and a little white pepper
500 ml (2 cups) hot rooibos tea made with 2 teabags
125 ml (½ cup) each cream and milk
croûtons for serving

Mix all the ingredients, except the tea, cream and milk, in a large, deep saucepan. Pour in the tea. Bring to the boil, then reduce the heat, cover and simmer slowly until the vegetables are cooked and soft – about 30 minutes. Cool. Remove the clove and cinnamon stick only when the soup is cold, so that their flavours can develop fully while they're cooling down. Whizz in a blender, in batches, until smooth. Return to the saucepan, and add the cream and milk. Check the seasoning, and heat through without boiling. Ladle into warmed soup bowls and sprinkle a few croûtons onto each serving. **Serves 6.**

* **Using only 1 clove might sound like a mistake, but it isn't – I find that 2 cloves just edge out the delicate flavours in this soup.**

CURRIED STAMPKORING SALAD

Stampkoring (or pearled whole wheat) is a nutty grain with a truly homespun appeal.
It takes longer to cook than rice, but the following method cuts down on time,
and in any case it's worth a little extra care to turn out this wholesome salad.
Serve as a bright item at any cold buffet, or at a braai, or for a summer lunch with
things on the side, like green leaves and avocado, yoghurt, hard-boiled eggs and chutney.

250 ml (1 cup) stampkoring
700 ml (2⅘ cups) water
2 ml (½ tsp) turmeric
5 ml (1 tsp) sea salt and a dash of oil
60 ml (¼ cup) oil
1 large onion, sliced into thin rings
½ red pepper, seeded and diced
2 cloves garlic, crushed
3 courgettes (baby marrows) (150 g),
pared and very finely diced
15 ml (1 Tbsp) curry powder
5 ml (1 tsp) ground cumin
2 ml (½ tsp) ground coriander
60 ml (4 Tbsp) seedless raisins
30 ml (2 Tbsp) chopped fresh
coriander leaves and stems
60 ml (4 Tbsp) sunflower seeds

Rinse the stampkoring and soak, generously covered in cold water, for at least 2 hours. Bring the 700 ml (2⅘ cups) water to the boil in a deep, heavy saucepan, adding the turmeric, salt and dash of oil. Drain the soaked stampkoring, tip into the boiling water, give it a quick stir, and reduce the heat to very low. Simmer, covered, for about 45 minutes, until the water is absorbed and the grains are soft. (Once ready, it will burn, so keep an eye on it.) Meanwhile, heat the 60 ml (¼ cup) oil in a large frying pan and add the onion, red pepper, garlic and courgettes. Toss until softening and glistening, then add all the spices and the raisins. Stir briefly over low heat until aromatic. If the stampkoring isn't ready, cover the frying pan and set aside. Tip the cooked stampkoring into a large bowl and immediately fork in the hot, spicy vegetables in oil. Add the coriander and sunflower seeds, check for salt and perhaps a little lemon juice, then set aside and, when it stops steaming, cover loosely. Serve at room temperature. The salad may also be refrigerated overnight, in a covered glass bowl. **Serves 4–8, depending on the occasion.**

Saucy, Crumb-Topped Baked Fish Fillets

This may be fairly quick and easy, but it's also deceptively rich and rather elegant.
The basics are fresh fish fillets, covered with a nutty/crumby/herby mixture
and baked on a mushroom-tomato sauce. The quantities are modest, and the flavours
quite mild – and yet, as you eat, they seem to develop and quietly introduce themselves,
and the end result is just hugely satisfying. Cape salmon and kabeljou (kob) are good choices,
and the fillets must be skinned, so that all the flavours can penetrate.

4 large, skinned fish fillets, about 700 g
sea salt and milled black pepper
slivers of butter

SAUCE

30 ml (2 Tbsp) oil
2 leeks, thinly sliced
250 g mushrooms,
white or brown, chunked
400 g ripe and juicy tomatoes,
skinned and chopped
sea salt, milled black pepper
and a pinch of sugar

TOPPING

3 thin slices crustless bread,
white or brown, and rather stale
1 slim slice onion
grated rind of ½ large lemon
24 unblanched almonds
a small handful of parsley tufts
3 ml (a rounded ½ tsp) dried dill
(or about 15 ml (1 Tbsp) chopped
fresh dill)
15 ml (1 Tbsp) oil

To make the sauce, heat the oil and soften
the leeks, then add the mushrooms, tomatoes,
seasoning and sugar. Cover and simmer for about
15 minutes, stirring now and then to mash up
the tomatoes; the result should be a juicy sauce,
not thick. Pour into a medium-sized baking dish
to cover the bottom quite thickly.

To make the topping, put the bread, onion,
lemon rind, almonds, parsley and dill into the bowl
of a processor fitted with the metal blade. Process
until very finely crumbed, then add the oil and
pulse just until moistened. Place the fish *on top*
of the tomato sauce and season lightly, then
spread the crumb mixture over the top of each
fillet, patting down lightly and dividing equally.
Arrange a few slivers of butter on top and bake
at 180 °C for 25–30 minutes, or until the fish is
just cooked through. Serve with the sauce and a
green veg or salad and, if that's not enough, you
could boil a few potatoes, slice them into wedges,
brush with a little oil and bake at the same time
as the fish. **Serves 4.**

SIMPLY SUPER FISH DISH

At heart this is a basic, well-known oldie from every Granny's cookbook:
hake, mushroom sauce and cheese, but an updated spin on the ingredients results
in something really special. In this recipe, chunky portabellini mushrooms add
amazing texture to the creamy sauce, which is poured over a whole side of firm-textured
yellowtail. The topping of cheddar remains, and the quick browning under the grill.
If preferred, use another type of mushroom, or fish, but this combination is really good.

1 side of yellowtail, skinned
and filleted, 600–700 g
(prepared weight)
sea salt and fresh lemon juice
uncoloured, grated cheddar cheese
for topping

SAUCE
15 ml (1 Tbsp) oil and a nut of butter
1 bunch spring onions or 2 bunching
onions, chopped
250 g portabellini mushrooms,
wiped and quartered
a pinch of dried dill
30 ml (2 Tbsp) flour
375 ml (1½ cups) milk
(preferably low-fat, it's a rich dish)
10 ml (2 tsp) Dijon mustard
10 ml (2 tsp) tomato paste
a pinch each of sea salt and sugar

Place the fish, skinned side up, in a lightly oiled baking dish in which it will lie flat. Season lightly and sprinkle with lemon juice, then bake at 180 °C until just cooked through; test with a fork – yellowtail, especially, dries out if overcooked.

While the fish is in the oven, make the sauce. Heat the oil and butter in a heavy saucepan, add the onions, mushrooms and dill, and cook, tossing gently over low heat, for several minutes, then sprinkle in the flour. When absorbed, slowly stir in the milk, then the mustard and tomato paste. Allow to bubble away over low heat for a few minutes until you have a medium-thick, faintly pink sauce. Season as necessary, and pour the sauce over the cooked fish. Sprinkle modestly with cheese and slide under a preheated grill until golden brown. This happens very quickly, so don't go away. Serve with brown rice and a green veg, or a salad. **Serves 4.**

BIG JOE'S CHICKEN CASSEROLE

Colourful comfort food – everyday ingredients, lots of sauce,
slightly tangy, slightly sweet and perfect with mash and veg.

a dash of oil
1–1.2 kg braai pack of free-range chicken, trimmed
sea salt and a few grinds of black pepper
1 large onion, finely chopped
2 medium carrots, finely diced
45 ml (3 Tbsp) flour
250 ml (1 cup) chicken stock
1 x 410 g can chopped, peeled tomatoes
15 ml (1 Tbsp) tomato paste
30 ml (2 Tbsp) whole grain mustard
45 ml (3 Tbsp) Mrs Ball's chutney
10 ml (2 tsp) Worcestershire sauce
20 ml (4 tsp) caramel brown sugar
60 ml (4 Tbsp) seedless raisins
a little sea salt
chopped parsley for sprinkling

Heat just a slick of oil in a frying pan and brown the chicken lightly, skin side first, to release any excess fat. Arrange the pieces, skin side down and fairly close together, in a large baking dish, deep enough to take the generous sauce. Season lightly. Add the onion and carrots to the pan drippings and toss over a low heat until just starting to colour and soften, then sprinkle in the flour. When absorbed, add the stock, tomatoes, tomato paste, mustard, chutney, Worcestershire sauce, sugar, raisins and salt. Stir to mix while bringing to the boil. Pour over the chicken, which should be almost completely covered by the sauce. Cover the dish with a lid, or with a sheet of greaseproof paper and then foil, and bake at 160 °C for 1¼ hours. Turn the chicken pieces, increase the oven temperature to 180 °C and bake, uncovered, for a further 15–20 minutes. If the sauce looks at all greasy, simple flick a paper kitchen towel over the top. Sprinkle with parsley and serve. **Serves 5–6.**

SPICY LAMB, BUTTER BEAN AND CAULI CURRY

Call it old-fashioned, but this is just the stuff that memories are made of –
warming, comforting food without any disconcerting frills. And it really is *very* good.
The only possible hiccup is the need for an exceptionally wide saucepan so that
the ingredients don't lie on top of each other, but can wallow in the lovely sauce.
Otherwise it's hassle-free.

8 lamb chump chops (800 g) (not braai
chops, but those meaty little slabs
with a tiny marrow bone in the centre)
30 ml (2 Tbsp) oil
1 large onion, sliced into thin rings
1 small red chilli,
seeded and chopped
15 ml (1 Tbsp) curry powder
5 ml (1 tsp) ground cumin
2 ml (½ tsp) each ground cinnamon
and turmeric
30 ml (2 Tbsp) flour
375 ml (1½ cups) hot beef stock
150 ml (⅝ cup) tomato purée
2 cloves garlic, crushed
sea salt and a little sugar
1 x 410 g can butter beans,
rinsed and drained
200 g small cauliflower florets
a generous sprinkling of fresh
coriander leaves

Slice the chops in half. Bring the oil to a gentle heat in that very large pan. Add the onion, chilli and all the spices, toss briefly, just until smelling gorgeous, then add the lamb and brown on both sides. If the spices start to scorch, add just a dribble of water, but do brown the lamb well. Reduce the heat to very low and sprinkle in the flour. Toss, and when the flour has been absorbed, slowly add the stock, tomato purée, garlic, salt and sugar. Cover, and simmer over very low heat for 1 hour, stirring from time to time. Mix in the butter beans and cauliflower – there should be no need to add extra liquid, the slow simmer should have resulted in a medium-thick, plentiful sauce. Cover, and simmer for a further 20 minutes or so, to cook the cauliflower, then check the seasoning. If it is tart, add a dribble of honey, it does wonders; and if time allows, and you are using a non-reactive pan, allow the curry to cool down a bit. Reheat just before serving, sprinkle with the coriander, and serve from the pan with yellow rice and chutney. **Serves 4–6.**

Mushroom and Spinach Noodle Bake

A layered pasta casserole is a fine example of comfort food, and this dish,
with its succulent mix of vegetables, noodles and a blanket of sauce has a lot
more style than macaroni cheese. As it can be completely assembled in advance,
and sits very well alongside a salad and bread, it offers a happy choice for informal entertaining.

30 ml (2 Tbsp) olive oil

1 large onion, finely chopped

2–3 cloves garlic, crushed

1 small or ½ large green pepper, seeded and diced

250 g brown mushrooms, wiped and sliced

2 ml (½ tsp) dried mixed herbs

250 g ripe tomatoes, skinned and chopped

15 ml (1 Tbsp) tomato paste

5 ml (1 tsp) each sea salt and sugar

a grind of black pepper

2 bay leaves

60 ml (¼ cup) red wine

500 ml (2 cups) shredded baby spinach

200 g spinach tagliatelle

grated nutmeg and parmesan cheese for topping

CHEESE SAUCE

30 ml (2 Tbsp) oil and a nut of butter

45 ml (3 Tbsp) flour

5 ml (1 tsp) mustard powder

500 ml (2 cups) warmed full-cream or low-fat milk

100 g cheddar cheese, grated

sea salt and white pepper

Heat the oil in a large frying pan. Add the onion, garlic and green pepper, toss until softening, then add the mushrooms and herbs. Reduce the heat and toss until aromatic, then add the remaining ingredients, except the spinach and pasta and topping. Cover and simmer, stirring off and on to mash up the tomatoes. Keep the heat very low to retain the succulence – 15 minutes should do it – and just before it comes off the heat, remove the bay leaves, stir in the spinach and allow it to wilt. While the sauce is simmering, cook and drain the pasta.

Make a white sauce as usual, adding the cheese and seasoning last. Lightly oil a *deep* baking dish, about 28 x 18 x 6 cm. Cover the base with half the vegetable sauce, top with half the noodles; repeat the layers, then pour the cheese sauce over the top, to cover. Sprinkle with a little nutmeg, and then parmesan, and bake at 180 °C for 35 minutes. Leave to settle for 10 minutes before serving. **Serves 6.**

CUSTARD TART

Closely linked to an unbaked *melktert* but with unexpected touches – like the crumb crust instead of pastry, and the crunchy almond topping. It's not as fluffy as a *melktert*, and making the custard does require some care, but the result is a good, smooth-textured, orange or lemon tart. Perfect for a simple, quickly made dessert, or instead of cake for tea.

CRUST
125 ml (½ cup) fine biscuit crumbs
30 ml (2 Tbsp) melted butter

FILLING
500 ml (2 cups) milk
10 ml (2 tsp) butter
30 ml (2 Tbsp) cake flour
30 ml (2 Tbsp) cornflour
90 ml (6 Tbsp) castor sugar
a large pinch of sea salt
5 ml (1 tsp) very finely grated orange rind (about 1 large orange), or
2 ml (½ tsp) very finely grated lemon rind (about ½ large lemon)
2 XL free-range eggs
5 ml (1 tsp) vanilla essence
toasted almond flakes and ground cinnamon for the topping

To make the crust, mix the crumbs and melted butter and press firmly onto the base of a lightly buttered pie dish, 18 cm diameter, with sloping sides – the old-fashioned glass pie dish, in fact. Bake for 10 minutes at 180 °C, then cool.

To make the filling you'll need a deep, medium-sized, really heavy saucepan. Rinse with water – this helps to prevent the milk from scorching. Heat half the milk with half the butter. Meanwhile, whizz the remaining milk, the cake flour, cornflour, castor sugar, salt, orange or lemon rind and eggs in a blender until smoothly mixed. Pour into the heated milk and then stir continuously, over *low* heat, until the mixture starts to thicken. At this stage, it's best to use a balloon whisk to achieve a smooth, lump-free custard. When it starts to pop and becomes as thick as really dense porridge, remove from the stove, beat in the remaining butter and the vanilla essence and pour onto the crust. Work quickly, as the custard firms up quickly. Spread evenly, and immediately sprinkle with the almonds and dust with cinnamon. Cool, then refrigerate before serving. **Makes 8 wedges.**

Green Fig and Ginger Cheesecake

Fig and ginger preserves combine superbly, and here they add amazing
flavour and an ethnic touch to a plump, fluffy cheesecake.

CRUST

125 ml (½ cup) each ginger biscuit and
plain biscuit crumbs

75 ml (5 Tbsp) melted butter

FILLING

25 ml (5 tsp) gelatine

75 ml (5 Tbsp) cold water

a knob or two of ginger preserve*

1 x 370 g jar green fig preserve*

2 XL free-range egg whites

200 ml (⅘ cup) castor sugar

250 g cream cheese

250 g smooth, low-fat cottage cheese

250 ml (1 cup) cream

7 ml (1½ tsp) vanilla essence

sliced figs and ground cinnamon for
topping

*** It is important to pat the preserves
quite dry, so that they don't 'weep',
and if chilling overnight, the crust
will soften but this won't affect the
delicious flavour.**

Mix the biscuit crumbs and butter, press firmly onto the greased base of a fairly deep 22–23 cm pie dish, and chill.

To make the filling, sponge the gelatine in the cold water, then dissolve over simmering water. Rinse off the syrup, pat dry and finely chop enough ginger and figs to give you 30 ml (2 Tbsp) of each, and set aside. Whisk the egg whites until stiffening, then gradually whisk in *half* the castor sugar to make a glossy meringue. Whisk the remaining castor sugar with both tubs of cheese, the cream and the vanilla essence until smooth. Slowly, while whisking, add the cooled gelatine, then fold in the meringue. Pour half this mixture onto the chilled crust. Sprinkle over the chopped ginger and fig preserve, then cover with the remaining creamy mixture, spreading evenly. (Work quickly as it firms up fast.) Chill until set. Rinse, pat dry and slice 3–4 of the remaining figs into thin rounds, arrange in a circle round the edge of the cheesecake and sprinkle the centre with cinnamon – either do this just before serving, or decorate and chill again until required, although the colour will then fade a bit. Slice into wedges and carefully remove with a spatula. **Serves 10.**

BAKED SAUCY CHOC-NUT PUDDING

A sweet and fudgy old-timer; serve hot, in syrupy scoops, over vanilla ice cream.

60 g very soft butter
125 ml (½ cup) castor sugar
1 XL free-range egg
5 ml (1 tsp) vanilla essence
250 ml (1 cup) cake flour
5 ml (1 tsp) baking powder
2 ml (½ tsp) ground cinnamon
a small pinch of sea salt
20 ml (4 tsp) cocoa powder
80 ml (⅓ cup) milk
40–50 g chopped walnuts

SAUCE
125 ml (½ cup) light brown sugar
15 ml (1 Tbsp) cocoa powder
300 ml (1⅕ cups) boiling water

Using an electric whisk, cream the butter and castor sugar until pale. Beat the egg with the vanilla essence and whisk into the butter mixture, combining to a soft, smooth consistency. Sift the flour, baking powder, cinnamon, salt and cocoa right into the creamed mixture. Give a quick whisk to combine, then add the milk and give another quick whisk to smooth out. Fold in the walnuts and then turn the batter – which will be quite thick – into a lightly buttered 20 cm pie dish (not less than 5 cm deep, as once it's in the oven the syrup will gurgle and bubble up quite fiercely round the edges).

Stir together the ingredients for the sauce and, as soon as the sugar has dissolved, pour carefully over the batter. Bake at 180 °C for 25 minutes, until risen and firm. **Serves 6.**

Sylvie's Biscuit Tin

All the biscuits are made using an electric whisk.

Honeyed gingers

Very moreish caramel-coloured cookies, made with really basic ingredients.

250 ml (1 cup) cake flour
15 ml (1 Tbsp) ground ginger
a pinch of salt
1 ml (¼ tsp) ground cinnamon
125 ml (½ cup) light brown sugar
125 ml (½ cup) wholewheat flour
125 g soft butter
5 ml (1 tsp) bicarbonate of soda
15 ml (1 Tbsp) honey
30 ml (2 Tbsp) hot water

Sift the cake flour, ginger, salt and cinnamon. Add the sugar and wholewheat flour. Mix in the butter, whisking until the mixture resembles fine crumbs. Mix the bicarb and honey into the water and, when it fizzes, mix into the flour mixture. Mix well to a soft dough. Shape into a ball, pinch off pieces, roll into balls and place on baking sheets that have been first oiled and then lined with two sheets* of baking paper, leaving room for spreading. Press down with a fork, and bake at 180 °C for 18–20 minutes until a rich caramel colour. Carefully remove to a rack to cool. **Makes 20.**

* With ovens that heat from below, biscuits easily get overbrowned bottoms. Lining baking trays with a double layer of baking paper usually prevents this.

Jumbo oat crisps

Big as small saucers, flat, crunchy and wholesome,
these are best made in relays because they spread with such abandon.

125 g very soft butter
125 ml (½ cup) oil
250 ml (1 cup) granulated sugar
250 ml (1 cup) oats
250 ml (1 cup) wholewheat flour
125 ml (½ cup) cake flour
125 ml (½ cup) desiccated coconut
a pinch of salt
5 ml (1 tsp) bicarbonate of soda
15 ml (1 Tbsp) hot water
45–60 ml (3–4 Tbsp) currants
60 ml (4 Tbsp) sunflower seeds
5 ml (1 tsp) vanilla essence

Whisk together the butter, oil, sugar, oats, both flours, coconut and salt, combining well to make a soft dough. Dissolve the bicarbonate of soda in the hot water and add, mixing well, then mix in the currants, sunflower seeds and vanilla essence. Shape the mixture into a ball with your hands, then pinch off pieces and shape into flat patties by tossing between your palms. The dough is very sticky, and this is the best way to handle it. Place the patties on oiled, double-lined baking sheets, leaving *plenty* of room for spreading. Press down lightly with a fork, and bake at 180 °C for 15 minutes until they have grown into large, flat, golden-brown discs. As they will be very soft, leave on the trays to crisp for a few minutes, then use a spatula to remove to cooling racks. **Makes 21 – or more, if you prefer to make smaller crisps.**

Butter pecan snaps

A rich, crunchy picture-book cookie.

250 g soft butter

250 ml (1 cup) castor sugar

1 large free-range egg, beaten

5 ml (1 tsp) vanilla essence

750 ml (3 cups) flour – plain white,
or cake, or half and half

5 ml (1 tsp) bicarbonate of soda

5 ml (1 tsp) ground cinnamon

2 ml (½ tsp) grated nutmeg

a pinch of sea salt

100 g pecan nuts, chopped

Cream the butter and castor sugar until light and pale. Beat in the egg and vanilla essence. Sift in, all together, the flour, bicarb, spices and salt, and whisk to make a soft dough. Add the pecans and, using your hands, work the mixture into a ball. Pinch off pieces and roll into fairly large marbles – the dough is very soft and it will be necessary to flour your hands now and then. Place well apart on baking sheets, first oiled and then lined with two layers of baking paper. Flatten lightly with a fork, and bake at 160 °C for 18–20 minutes until the cookies have spread into discs and are just beginning to brown round the edges. Use a spatula to transfer to a rack to cool. **Makes 48.**

Ouma's Aniseed Buttermilk Rusks

The favourite, old-fashioned, morning coffee dunk,
neither too sweet nor buttery for so early in the day.

500 g self-raising flour
5 ml (1 tsp) salt
2 ml (½ tsp) baking powder
125 ml (½ cup) sugar
10 ml (2 tsp) aniseed, coarsely
crushed with a rolling pin
125 g soft butter
1 XL free-range egg
200 ml (⅘ cup) buttermilk

Sift the flour, salt and baking powder into a large bowl, then mix in the sugar and aniseed. Rub in the butter until finely crumbled. Or melt the butter, which is quicker, and works just as well, and mix into the flour mixture before adding the remaining ingredients. Whisk the egg into the buttermilk, pour into the flour mixture, mix well and then start to knead. The more you knead, the better the rusks will rise. If the dough becomes sticky (which is unlikely), flour your hands as necessary; if too dry, add a drop more buttermilk, but be careful of making too soft a dough. Continue kneading until it forms a smooth, elastic ball and leaves the sides of the bowl clean. Break off eight equal pieces and work each one into a smooth, round ball. Place the balls up against each other in a medium-sized loaf tin (20 x 10 x 7 cm is just right) first brushed with oil and then lined, base and sides, with baking paper. Bake at 200 °C for 20 minutes, then at 180 °C for 30 minutes; test by poking a skewer into the centre. Leave to stand for 10 minutes before turning out onto a rack; remove paper, and leave until cool enough to handle. Break the balls apart, and then, with the help of a knife, nick and break open again – try not to cut right through, just here and there, and then break into rusk shapes. Place in a single layer on a baking sheet lined with several sheets of baking paper, and dry out in a very low oven, about 100 °C, turning once. **Makes about 32, depending on size.**

Easy Wholewheat Bread with Seeds and Raisins

An undisputed favourite, an any time nibbly bread that delights and fills up
children and adults alike. It's quick to make, and goes with everything any time of the day,
but raisins may be left out if serving with a savoury dish.

4 x 250 ml (4 cups) wholewheat flour

250 ml (1 cup) white bread flour

1 x 10 g sachet instant dried yeast

7 ml (1½ tsp) salt

90 ml (6 Tbsp) sunflower seeds

30 ml (2 Tbsp) sesame seeds

125 ml (½ cup) seedless raisins
(optional)

30 ml (2 Tbsp) oil

15 ml (1 Tbsp) each molasses and
honey, or all honey, or all molasses*

about 500 ml (2 cups) very warm,
but not hot water**

sunflower seeds, sesame seeds
and poppy seeds for topping

* Molasses adds colour, flavour,
iron and minerals; give it a try.
** The only pitfall in making this
bread lies in using water that is
either too cold or too hot – in
either case the yeast won't rise.
The water should be hotter than
lukewarm but definitely not hot
enough to make coffee. Practice
will soon make perfect.

In a large bowl, mix both the flours, the yeast, salt, seeds and raisins. Stir together the oil and molasses and/or honey, and mix in well. Mix in 250 ml (1 cup) of the warm water. Slowly add the remaining water, or just enough to make a soft and sticky batter – not sloppy, nor stiff. Oil the base and sides of a 26 x 9 x 7 cm loaf tin, then line with baking paper, base and sides. Spoon in the bread mixture, using a dampened wooden spoon to press in firmly and evenly and smooth the top. Sprinkle with the seeds in diagonal stripes, for a professional look, and leave in a warm place to rise until just over the top of the tin. In winter this could take as long as 1 hour. Bake at 200 °C for 30 minutes, then at 180 °C for 20 minutes. Stand a few minutes, then turn out, remove paper and knock on the bottom – if it sounds hollow, it's done. Now cool on a rack or, if you want to crisp the sides, return to the switched-off oven, out of the tin and upside down, for about 10 minutes.

Amatilda

'I saw it with my own eyes. But don't ask me *what*,' she said, licking her third finger and pointing it heavenward, as though testing the wind, 'because as true's my name's Sophia, I can never tell you. Not you, Anna, or anyone. Not until my dying day.'

Anna said nothing, she just stood at Sophia's front gate, waiting patiently, knowing that sooner or later it would all come out.

'Just now somebody hears me and then what?' Sophia's eyes darted this way and that. The street was deserted, but she nevertheless cupped her hand over her mouth. 'If somebody hears me,' she whispered, 'you might as well bury me, *finish klaar*, right here in the ground among my flowers.'

Anna waited.

'The trouble is,' Sophia lowered her head, leaning closer, 'the trouble is, a secret is like a fly in a bottle. It won't lie down, and it won't go away. It just buzzes there all the time, round and round and round, until in the end you can't think of anything else. You know how it is.'

Anna nodded.

'But what I always say is "A Secret Shared is A Secret Halved", so I'll just tell you quickly and get it over with. But remember …'

Sophia drew her finger across her tightly pursed lips.

Anna waited. 'It's Servaas.'

'Maria's Servaas?'

'Maria's Servaas. Him and Amatilda.'

'Oh my hat, Maria. Don't tell me. I don't want to hear it.'

'You don't want to hear it? Are you sure?'

'Yes. Go on.'

Sophia took a deep breath. 'He ... he ...' She started to sweat.

Droplets came out on her forehead like late-morning dew, ran down her pleated face, fell on her neck and disappeared into the poly-printed blouse. 'Servaas walked into the Coffee Shop and ...' she paused to watch a dog crossing the road. 'Well, he walked into the shop, made straight for Amatilda and slapped her on her – you know what – he slapped her under her apron ... but behind. Which isn't so bad as otherwise ... But I saw, and I said to him 'Servaas, I saw you, and after you've been married all these years to one of the finest ladies in Corriebush. *Ag*, no Servaas!'

And he said, 'I just wanted a cup of coffee, and I wanted it quickly, so what's wrong with that? A slap for a coffee?'

'Slap for a coffee my foot. Why can't you just order at the counter like other people?'

Sophia would have been even more shocked had she known that Servaas, with his slap, had slipped a pound note into Amatilda's belt, whispering, 'For last week's balls.'

From the day Amatilda had arrived in Corriebush in her yellow Beetle, the women had been uneasy about her presence.

'She comes here just like that, no connections in the district, a woman on her own. Just pops into town and quick as a wink buys Johnny's Club for cash. Now what does a person make of that?'

Purchasing The Club was not, however, the only reason for their ruffled feathers. Amatilda was an extraordinarily beautiful woman. She had huge violet eyes, and chestnut hair that fell to her shoulders in a flurry of curls. She always wore lipstick and earrings, and sometimes a hat and pearls when she went shopping, tripping down the street in a soft halo of perfume.

'Breath of the city,' one remarked.

'Breath of no good if you ask me,' said another, and for a long time none of them would set foot in the Coffee Shop even though they peered inquisitively through the windows when they passed.

'Must say it looks nice and clean,' they agreed.

'All those little tables with pink cloths and napkins to match. Flowers in the middle. Calendars on the walls. They say she's in there early in the mornings, dusting and polishing.'

'I hear she makes very good scones.'

'And cinnamon pancakes.'

'I wonder what she's done with the old snooker table?'

'At least THAT'S not a problem anymore.'

A few years before Amatilda's arrival, a farmer by the name of Johnny Smit decided to retire to town. Johnny had been a widower for many years and was beginning to find life on the farm altogether too much.

'All on my own there, and I'm not getting any younger you know, so it seems the sensible thing to do.'

And when Number Three came up for sale, he bought it and moved in. But in no time Johnny was bored.

'No windmills to fix, no sheep to dip, no lucerne to bale, I really need to get my teeth into something.'

And so he moved the rooms around a bit, knocked out one wall, bought some new furniture and opened The Club in Number Three, operating from five in the afternoons until eight at night every day except Sundays, and no women allowed.

The notice he put in the window read: Attention! Attention! This Club is an invitation to all the men of Corriebush who would like to roll up their sleeves, light a cigar, and have a little innocent fun at the end of the day. See the other window for opening times, and no wives. (signed) J. T. Smit, owner and proprietor.

Johnny laid on snooker and poker and darts, and a small pub in one corner, and in no time the place was buzzing. Some of the men went a couple of times a week. Some went every afternoon. It was a new experience, this, sitting down with their friends, having a round together, playing games, telling jokes. Johnny's Club was always noisy, loud with laughter and thick with smoke. The men loved it, and their wives rose up like a flock of angry buzzards.

'What's wrong with sitting at home drinking coffee on their own stoeps?' they asked each other angrily.

'Who knows what they might get up to, drinking into the night?'

'Playing cards for money?'

'Telling rude stories?'

'You know what they're like when they get together.'

They needed to take action and so they worked out a plan, simple as pie. Their men could go to Johnny's Club if that's what they wanted, but when they got home the supper table would have been cleared, and their wives asleep in bed. No food, and no foxtrot. Day after day, week after week. It worked like a dream.

'You know, James,' said Servaas, plucking his dart from the board. 'I've got a problem at home, and even hitting the bull's eye doesn't make me feel good anymore.'

'If it's what I think it is, then I have it too,' said James.

Asking around, they found that every Club member was having the same trouble.

'Cold food, cold women. Time to hands up, boys.'

And so the Corriebush men admitted defeat and went back to their pipes and sundowner coffees on their own stoeps. Johnny Smit's married daughter felt sorry for him and persuaded him to come and live with her in Port Elizabeth. And so Number Three stood empty. Until Amatilda burst into town, bought Number Three, and turned it into the Coffee Shop, which immediately became the women's new threat.

'You watch. The men will be there all day, like bees round a honey pot. Never mind that at home they can have tea and cake without having to pay for it.'

'It's her looks you have to watch out for. My mother always said no man can resist a pretty face, and she knew what she was talking about because my father ran away with one.'

'If it's not one thing, it's another. If it's not Johnny and his brandy, it's Amatilda and her cups of coffee.'

And yet – one had to hand it to the women of Corriebush – their hearts were warm and not unfair, and as the months passed they gradually softened. Amatilda was undeniably charming.

'She's so cheerful and friendly a person can't just look the other way. Even if you're on the other side of the street she waves and calls hello.'

'I hear she gives pensioners tea for nothing if they order cake.'

'And I must say the pot plants she puts on the pavement do look very pretty.'

'And she does keep to herself after hours.'

'You shouldn't judge a bird by its feathers, I always say.'

And after a few weeks they were all dropping in for morning coffee or afternoon tea.

It was a slow beginning, but everything was going surprisingly well until Amatilda started Friday Evening Circle.

Suddenly one day there were little printed cards tucked under the sugar bowls on each table. They read: Starting next week, 7 pm sharp. Men only. Lots of fun and surprises. Only six at a time, so booking is essential. See you! Love, Amatilda.

The women passed the cards round. From table to table and then from house to house. They were scandalized.

'Coffee and tea, fine. But this?'

The clucking and fretting went on for a while, and then they decided that only by taking a really firm stand would they stop their men.

'We'll tell them that if they go it's *finish klaar*.'

'We'll lock them out on Friday nights.'

'Shut them in on Friday nights.'

'Tell the *dominee*.'

Their men simply ignored them. Every Friday evening, six husbands would walk out of their front doors and straight to Number Three. After the last man had entered, the lights would be dimmed, and the curtains drawn.

The women – Lily and Maria, Anna and Sophia, Nellie and Amelia – were confounded.

'It's terrible to think that *all* our husbands are taking part,' said Lily.

'Terrible,' agreed Maria. 'And Servaas always wears his Sunday shirt!'

'When James creeps in at ten, I can smell her perfume on him.'

'Last week Charlie took a whole handful of food money out of the tin in the pantry with him. I saw him.'

'One woman, six men? Every week? It's a disgrace, if what I think it is is what it is.'

'Well, if it isn't what it is, then what is it?'

'If only I knew *exactly* what they were doing.'

'Come now Sophia, you weren't born yesterday.'

For a while they hoped that there might be a decent explanation, but when none was forthcoming, the fight simply went out of them and a dull resignation and sadness took its place. Until the Friday night that Bronnie Evans entered Number Three – and exposed them all.

Bronnie was the local librarian, a studious, serious woman who had never married and lived with her old mother in a cottage behind the library. On this particular Friday evening, Bronnie had arranged for the children taking part in the annual nativity play to come to a rehearsal in the Reading Room. They had just started, and were busy draping a blanket over one of the benches to look like a sheep, when the lights went out. Bronnie rushed to her cottage for candles, which helped a little, but she could not see well enough to read her notes and the children were showing signs of nerves, so she locked them in and went in search of Daniel, the town's engineer.

'Oh dear, Bronnie, he's at … at … Amatilda's, I'm afraid. You know how it is.' Amelia looked weepy. 'I can't fetch him, but perhaps you can? You'll find him there all right, Bronnie. Just tell him it's urgent.'

At last Amelia saw a glimmer of hope.

Bronnie did not have to be let in. She found the door unlocked so she gently pushed it open, her heart fluttering all over the place because she had heard that certain men were up to no good on Friday nights in there. But she wouldn't turn back now. There were the children waiting in the dark library, and poor Amelia weeping. So she quietly edged down the two steps and into the shop. It was empty.

There were noises, though, drifting up from downstairs. Men's voices, Amatilda's, a bit of laughter, soft music, a sudden loud exclamation. Bronnie had read a lot of books, some of them quite naughty, for her. And so she did have an inkling of the shock that could be in store. Nevertheless, she was deliciously terrified of what she might be about to see, so she inched her way to the top of the staircase to take a look.

What she saw was six men sitting round the old snooker table, knitting.

In front of them, all over the green baize, lay parts of cardigans and balls of brightly coloured wool, little piles of buttons, and needles scattered like fiddlesticks. And Amatilda was walking round and round helping and advising. 'You'd want to do a purl row now Servaas.'

'Yours is as good as done, Dawid, just the bobbles, and we'll be ready to wrap.'

'Oh dear, Charlie, you've dropped two stitches there, you've got a hole, here let me fix it.'

And then she saw Bronnie. 'Bronnie Evans, I don't know what the hell you're doing here, but if you go and tell these men's wives I'll burn all your books myself!'

Bronnie found her tongue. 'Please Daniel, I need you at the library, we're rehearsing the nativity play and the lights have gone out.'

'You go along Danny,' Amatilda said. 'I'll just sew up these sleeves.'

On the way to the library, Daniel explained to Bronnie, before she could ask.

'Nothing but innocent fun,' he said. 'For the price of a few skeins of wool and some buttons, Amatilda taught us how to knit.'

'To knit,' said Bronnie.

'To knit,' said Daniel. 'For the past few months she's had us sitting round the snooker table on Friday evenings, purling and plaining, buttonholing and stitching, while she helped us along and poured out the coffee. It was jolly good fun,' said Daniel.

'Jolly good fun,' said Bronnie.

'Tonight was our final lesson, because of Christmas Day being on Sunday.'

'Christmas on Sunday,' repeated Bronnie, her nerves still in shock.

Back at Number Three, the knitters were putting the finishing touches to the cardigans for their wives. Servaas held up his completed garment, a pale pink, with heart-shaped buttons.

'I just hope it fits,' he said. 'Or all this hard work for nothing.'

'Come now Servaas, you know you've enjoyed it,' Amatilda retorted, which was the signal for Herman to stand up and propose a vote of thanks. James had brought a magnum of sparkling wine, and after the speech they drank a toast to Amatilda.

'Oh, get on with you now,' she said. 'It was nothing.'

On Christmas morning six Corriebush wives found large, soft parcels under their Christmas trees. It is said that they wore their cardigans for the entire day, never mind the December heat, and on Boxing Day they put them on again and in a body walked to Number Three to thank Amatilda.

Some months later she sold the shop and left town.

'I want to travel,' she explained. 'I've made a bit of money now, and I'm thinking of Japan.'

They gave her a warm farewell party. 'When you think of what we thought at the beginning,' they said. 'Shame on us.'

As a parting gift they had ordered a length of pale green silk from Port Elizabeth and embroidered a shawl for her, each woman stitching a separate posy until the entire square was covered, like a field of brilliant flowers. Amatilda had it draped round her shoulders the day she left Corriebush in her yellow Beetle.

They had all gathered outside Number Three, wearing their Christmas jerseys, to see her off. Amatilda climbed in behind the wheel and started up the engine, and they all reached for the handkerchiefs up their sleeves. Amatilda leaned out of the window.

'*Ag*, no, you mustn't be sad,' she said. 'I'll bring you each a kimono.'

Then she blew them a kiss, and with a roar the Beetle rounded the corner and took the road that streaks north beside the old railway line.

Amatilda's Recipes

Amatilda loved to bake and when she opened her Coffee Shop, her aim was simply to provide good coffee and a selection of home-made treats to accompany the fragrant brew. She had a large glass showcase installed, and placed luscious little samples of her scones, cakes and cookies inside to tempt her customers. But as the success of the shop snowballed, the need for a larger menu became obvious because some customers were enjoying their morning visits so much that they were reluctant to leave and, having finished their coffee, simply sat there gossiping long after Amatilda had removed their cups and skittered from table to table, flicking the crumbs off the cloths into her pink plastic dustpan. Amatilda simply did not have the heart to shoo them away, so she decided it would make financial good sense to introduce a few savoury dishes for light lunches, and a dessert or two as well. 'Might as well let them make a meal of it,' she decided, and so she put a notice in the window. Due to popular demand, it read, this establishment will have an enlarged menu as from next Monday. Love, Amatilda. Everyone was delighted.

SAVOURY DEEP EGGS

Baked in ramekins, on a bed of freshly cooked tomatoes, bacon and corn,
and topped with cheese, this way of serving eggs makes a lovely change from
scrambled eggs and omelettes. They're also more convenient because they don't need
constant attention and are so easy to serve – one or two ramekins per person, with some hot
toast and butter. The size of the ramekins is quite important – 7 cm in diameter and 5 cm deep
(which is a fairly standard size), but if you don't have them, use a shallow baking dish instead.
Either way, these eggs are baked *au bain-marie* (the ramekins standing in a larger pan/tin of
simmering water). The quantities given are for 4 ramekins, but can easily be doubled or trebled.

10 ml (2 tsp) each oil and butter
4 rashers lean, rindless back bacon
(preferably unsmoked), diced
8 spring onions or slim baby leeks,
chopped
400 g ripe, fresh tomatoes,
skinned and chopped*
a few tufts of parsley, chopped
sea salt, milled black pepper and
a large pinch of sugar
80 ml (⅓ cup) cooked corn kernels
4 large or XL free-range eggs
grated cheddar cheese and
paprika for topping

* Use sweet and rosy fresh tomatoes
– canned won't do here.

Start by switching on the oven to 200 °C and at
the same time put in the pan/tin of water to heat
up, so that it's ready to take the ramekins when
they're ready. Heat the oil and butter in a medium-
sized frying pan and lightly sauté the bacon
and onions or leeks. Add the tomatoes, parsley,
seasoning and sugar and simmer, half-covered, for
about 15 minutes until fairly thick; stir occasionally
to mash up the tomatoes. If the mixture ends up
looking watery, simply take off the lid and turn up
the heat for a few minutes. Mix in the corn, check
the seasoning, then spoon into the ramekins,
dividing equally and levelly. Carefully break an
egg on top of each, cover generously with cheese,
dust with paprika, place in the pan/tin of hot water
– the ramekins should not touch – and bake for
about 20 minutes until the eggs are set and the
cheese melted. Grab a fork and tuck in at once.
Serves 2–4.

Egg, Cheese and Mushroom Bake

It's not quite a quiche, nor is it a tart, and it's not a frittata either,
nor can you call it an omelette. But it's useful.
Served with grilled tomatoes and hot toast, this easy bake slots
happily into the menu for a brunch or light lunch.

15 ml (1 Tbsp) oil
1 red pepper, seeded and snipped
into small pieces
200 g white mushrooms,
wiped and sliced
4 spring onions, plus some tops,
chopped
5 ml (1 tsp) chopped fresh
rosemary leaves
4 large free-range eggs
250 g smooth, low-fat cottage cheese
150 ml (⅔ cup) milk
45 ml (3 Tbsp) flour (absolutely level)
5 ml (1 tsp) mustard powder
a sprinkling of chopped parsley
100 g mature cheddar cheese, grated
salt and milled black pepper to taste
30 ml (2 Tbsp) dried, toasted
breadcrumbs for lining the pie dish
paprika for topping

Heat the oil and sauté the pepper, mushrooms, onions and rosemary until soft and aromatic; keep the heat low and stir around for about 10 minutes, or until the mixture is dry. Whisk together the eggs, cottage cheese, milk, flour, mustard powder, parsley, 75 g of the cheddar cheese, and the salt and pepper, then stir it into the vegetable mixture. Lightly oil a deep, 23 cm pie dish. Sprinkle with the breadcrumbs, swirl to coat and shake out the excess. Pour in the egg mixture. Let it settle evenly, then sprinkle with the remaining cheese and dust with paprika. Bake at 160 °C for 30–35 minutes, or until set. Stand for a minute or two before slicing into four large wedges. Remove with a spatula. **Serves 4.**

Coffee Shop Toasted Cheese Special

This is a favourite savoury munch, almost as quick to make as ordinary cheese toast,
but it *looks* much more appetising – all puffed up and golden brown on open slices of toast.
Delicious served with coffee for a hearty elevenses snack, or even a quick lunch.
Serve with knives and forks, 2 slices per customer.

200 g cheddar cheese, grated
2 ml (½ tsp) baking powder
2 XL free-range eggs, beaten
15 ml (1 Tbsp) whole grain mustard
a little sea salt and milled
black pepper
1 slim slice of onion, coarsely grated
20 ml (4 tsp) soft butter
wholewheat bread, sliced
2–3 tomatoes, thinly sliced
paprika for topping

Using a fork, mash the cheese, baking powder, eggs, mustard, seasoning, onion and butter together to make a coarse paste. Toast the bread on one side. Arrange a few slices of tomato on the untoasted side, and cover thickly with the cheese mixture. Dust with paprika, arrange on a heatproof platter and place under a hot grill – not too close, because the flavours have to come together, and there are eggs in there, and the cheese has to melt – but it takes only a few minutes to reach perfection. **Sufficient for 4–6 slices of bread, depending on size.**

Salad Platter with Blaaukrantz and Walnuts

… and roasted peppers, raw mushrooms and spinach, served with a whizzed blender dressing
and wholewheat rosemary and garlic ring bread. It's a treat.
And everything can be made in the *knip* of an eye, as Amatilda might have said.

250 g white mushrooms, just the
very tips of the stems removed,
then wiped and thinly sliced
60 ml (¼ cup) oil
30 ml (2 Tbsp) fresh lemon juice
1 clove garlic, crushed
2 red peppers, grilled, skinned,
then sliced into strips
4–6 spring onions, chopped,
or chopped, blanched baby leeks
150 g mixed salad leaves –
baby spinach, butter lettuce, etc.
a little sea salt
100 g Blaauwkrantz cheese, crumbled
40–50 g walnuts, toasted and
chopped (a light toasting or roasting
really makes a difference to the flavour)

Place the prepared mushrooms in a large glass bowl. (No salt at this stage.) Immediately toss with the oil, lemon juice and garlic. Mix in the red peppers and spring onions, cover and set aside or chill for up to 3 hours if working ahead. When ready to plate, line a large platter with the salad leaves. Spoon the mushroom mixture over evenly, salt lightly, then sprinkle with cheese and walnuts. **Serves 4.**

Blender dressing

250 ml (1 cup) oil
60 ml (¼ cup) white balsamic vinegar
(or half vinegar, half lemon juice)
a few tufts of parsley and celery leaves
5 ml (1 tsp) mustard powder
5 ml (1 tsp) Worcestershire sauce
10 ml (2 tsp) honey
a pinch of sea salt

Whizz all the ingredients together, pour into a decanter, and pass for diners to help themselves, along with the beautiful ring loaf, and butter.

Wholewheat rosemary and garlic ring bread

Mixed in minutes, this herby batter is turned into a tube tin where it billows into
a big, fat ring, and the aroma while baking will waft right through the house (or Coffee Shop).
This wholesome, moreish loaf slices well, and may also be baked in a regular loaf tin if preferred.

4 x 250 ml (4 cups) wholewheat flour*

250 ml (1 cup) white bread flour

1 x 10 g sachet instant dry yeast

7 ml (1½ tsp) sea salt

30 ml (2 Tbsp) finely chopped fresh
rosemary leaves

45–60 ml (3–4 Tbsp) chopped parsley

3 cloves garlic, crushed

4 spring onions, chopped

30 ml (2 Tbsp) oil

30 ml (2 Tbsp) treacle sugar

about 600 ml (2⅖ cups) warm water

* For a somewhat lighter loaf, use
750 ml (3 cups) wholewheat
flour and 500 ml (2 cups) white
bread flour – in this case
slightly less water is required.

Mix all the ingredients, except the water, in a large bowl. Slowly stir in just enough of the water to make a moist but not sloppy batter. The water should be warmer than lukewarm, but far from boiling hot. Turn into a 22 x 9 cm tube tin, oiled and lined with baking paper – base, sides and funnel – even if it's a non-stick tin. Use a dampened spatula to spread evenly. The batter should reach halfway up the sides. Cover lightly with a cloth and leave to rise in a warm place until doubled in size – about 30–40 minutes, depending on the weather. Bake at 200 °C for 30 minutes, then reduce heat to 180 °C and bake for a further 20–25 minutes, until risen and browned. Stand for a few minutes before turning out onto a rack to cool, using a spatula to ease it out if necessary. If baking as a loaf, use a 26 x 9 x 7 cm tin, oiled and lined, and do not cover when rising as the batter will stick to the cloth. It should rise to just over the top of the tin, and add about 10 minutes extra to the baking time. Stand for a few minutes before running a spatula round the sides to invert and cool.

Scrumptious Smoked Salmon Luncheon Salad

Diners frequently sit and look at this for some time before tucking in.
The colour-combination is just brilliant: creamy salmon, avocado, beetroot and rocket –
and yet this flamboyant salad is dead easy to prepare. All you have to cook is the beetroot.
Once that's over with, and the salmon mixture mixed, it's simply a matter of arranging
these wonderful ingredients attractively, either on one large platter or on
single-serving plates, along with a basket of sliced rye bread and a pot of butter. Fabulous.

1 bunch small to medium beetroot (600–700 g)
2 x 250 g tubs smooth, low-fat cottage cheese, drained if necessary
200–250 g smoked salmon, snipped (off-cuts are fine)
125 ml (½ cup) cultured sour cream
finely grated rind of ½ small lemon
6–8 slim spring onions, plus some tops, finely chopped
5 ml (1 tsp) Dijon mustard
a few drops of Tabasco sauce
about 60 g rocket and a pillow-pack of salad leaves, mixed
3–4 avocados
milled black pepper and chopped walnuts for topping

Scrub the beetroot gently so as not to break the skin and cut off the tops, but leave on 2 cm, then boil or roast – the latter is tastier, but takes longer. Cool, then skin and pat dry. Meanwhile, combine the cottage cheese, salmon, sour cream, lemon rind, onions, mustard and Tabasco. Refrigerate in a covered glass bowl for a few hours for the flavours to develop. Just before serving, slice the beetroot thinly and arrange around the edge of the platter. Next, make a circle of rocket and salad leaves. Then come the slices of avocado. The salmon mixture goes in the centre – pile it into one or more nice little bowls to make it easier to dip into. Top with freshly milled pepper and a good sprinkling of walnuts. (If the platter is too full already, put the bowls of salmon alongside.) If serving on one large platter, add a fork for spearing, and a spoon for the salmon dip.
Serves 6.

WHOLEWHEAT MINI-BREADS WITH FIG PRESERVE AND GOAT'S CHEESE

These sweetish little breads, looking for all the world like rocky brown muffins,
are made in a trice and are just the thing for a filler at brunch, or for a trendy little breakfast
with coffee. The minis, speckled with raisins and hinted with cinnamon,
simply beg for a glistening, syrupy preserved fig alongside, with a disc or two
of soft goat's cheese and a bowl of soft butter.

250 ml (1 cup) white bread flour
5 ml (1 tsp) bicarbonate of soda
5 ml (1 tsp) baking powder
5 ml (1 tsp) salt
5 ml (1 tsp) ground cinnamon
750 ml (3 cups) wholewheat flour
90 ml (6 Tbsp) seedless raisins
30 ml (2 Tbsp) treacle sugar
(or soft brown sugar)
30 ml (2 Tbsp) honey
20 ml (4 tsp) oil
500 ml (2 cups) buttermilk
milk for glazing
sunflower seeds for topping

Sift the white bread flour, bicarb, baking powder, salt and cinnamon into a large mixing bowl. Add the wholewheat flour, raisins and sugar. Whisk together the honey, oil and buttermilk; add to the flour mixture and stir until thoroughly combined. The mixture needs to be quite soft and sticky, and you might need to add a spoon or two of water (rinse out the buttermilk carton) so that it can be easily scooped into the muffin cups. Rather add too little than too much, though – the dough must not be wet and slippery. You will need large muffin cups (not paper cases) for these mini-breads – oil them lightly first and then divide the dough equally – don't try to make them flat, just leave them more or less as they drop. Brush the tops lightly with milk, sprinkle with sunflower seeds and bake at 180 °C for 25 minutes until well risen, firm, and rocky in appearance. Stand for about 10 minutes before carefully removing to a rack to cool. Best served on the same day, with the figs and the cheese. **Makes 12.**

Unsinkable Baked Lemon Cheesecake

A favourite cheesecake, soft and creamy, that does not make waves in the baking,
then collapse in the centre. The flat top, therefore, makes a perfect base for a spread
of whipped cream and a sprinkling of lightly candied lemon peel and ginger.
For a lighter option, the cream can be omitted – simply sprinkle the cheesecake
with ground cinnamon before baking.

CRUST

250 ml (1 cup) biscuit crumbs

60 ml (¼ cup) melted butter

FILLING

2 large free-range eggs

125 ml (½ cup) castor sugar

2 ml (½ tsp) vanilla essence

7 ml (1½ tsp) very finely grated
lemon rind (that's 1 whole,
thick-skinned lemon, well-washed
and carefully grated to exclude
any white pith)

30 ml (2 Tbsp) cornflour

2 x 250 g tubs smooth, low-fat
cottage cheese, drained of any liquid

150 ml (⅗ cup) thick cream

Mix the ingredients for the crust and press firmly onto the greased base (not the sides) of a 20 cm pie dish – use the back of a spoon to spread evenly. Bake at 160 °C for 10 minutes. Cool.

To make the filling, whisk the eggs and sugar until pale and light, then add the vanilla, lemon rind, cornflour, cheese and cream. Whisk well until everything's combined, then pour onto the crust. Bake on the middle shelf of the oven at 180 °C for 20 minutes, then switch off the heat but don't open the door – just leave it there for 15 minutes more before removing it to cool – it will still be a bit wobbly. Once cooled, refrigerate until firm enough to slice. **Makes 8 wedges.**

Candied lemon peel and ginger

Place in a small saucepan: 125 ml (½ cup) water; thinly julienned peel (or zest) of 1 medium lemon; peeled and very thinly sliced (about 10 ml (2 tsp)) fresh root ginger (about 1 small knob). Simmer, covered, for 10 minutes or until softened, then add 15 ml (1 Tbsp) light brown sugar. Increase the heat and boil, uncovered, until lightly caramelized, shaking the pan regularly. Remove from the stove when just starting to catch; carefully add 30 ml (2 Tbsp) water and leave to cool and soften further before sprinkling over the top of the cooled cheesecake.

FROZEN MAPLE, HONEY AND PECAN CREAMS

Amazing ingredients go into these sweet, luscious little igloos, which are just perfect
with poached mangoes*, served hot with the melting, mapley cream. Using paper cases
makes good sense. Frozen in this way, they can be turned out quickly onto little plates – or even
quaint saucers; this method also stretches the recipe, which is a good idea as it is so rich –
you can't treat it like ordinary ice cream. When napped (or flanked) with a spoon of warm fruit
(use pears when mangoes are out of season) they also look elegant, and taste superb.

60 ml (4 Tbsp) fat-free milk powder
60 ml (¼ cup) maple syrup
(pure if you can find it, otherwise
use the maple-flavoured one)
30 ml (2 Tbsp) pale, runny honey
(e.g. veldflower or fynbos)
175 ml (⅔ cup) plain Bulgarian yoghurt
(thick, not drinking yoghurt)
250 ml (1 cup) cream,
fairly softly whipped
60–90 ml (4–6 Tbsp) chopped
pecan nuts
a few drops of vanilla essence
1 XL egg white, stiffly whisked with
a pinch of salt

Put the milk powder into a freezer-friendly mixing
bowl – a large, bombe-shaped one is perfect.
Pour in the maple syrup and honey and beat
(using an electric whisk) until the milk powder
has completely dissolved; scrape down the sides
of the bowl when necessary. (If the bowl is free-
standing, hold it tightly while whisking – the
mixture is so stiff that it easily sets the bowl
spinning – one minute it's on the counter, the next
it's on the floor.) Stir in the yoghurt, then give it all
a quick whisk to combine, and place in the freezer
until just firm, *not* solid. Remove from the freezer
and beat again and, when smooth, fold in the
cream, nuts and vanilla. Stir a dollop of the stiff
egg white through, then fold in the remainder.
Place 10 large paper cases in the hollows of
a muffin pan, spoon the mixture into the cases,
dividing equally, and freeze. Cover loosely,
and they will hold their flavour for several days.
Makes 10.

* Poach the fruit lightly – don't let it get mushy.
Just chop up one or two ripe mangoes
chunkily, and heat through in the minimum
of water with the minimum of sugar, for about
3 minutes. Pears will take a little longer.

STRAWBERRY AND MINT SOFT-SERVES

This is quickly whizzed in a blender to a pink, thick creaminess, like a soft-serve,
but instead of coming in a cone (as one would expect in a Coffee Shop),
the mixture is spooned into parfait or wine glasses or goblets,
and refrigerated until just firm enough to be scooped up with small spoons.
The minimum quantity of gelatine is used to achieve the softly set texture,
while the elusive fragrance of fresh mint (just a snitch is necessary) comes through
now and then to offset the richness. This dessert is a real quick 'n easy,
and offers a slightly new take on the popular combo of strawberries and cream.

500 g ripe, bright red strawberries
10 ml (2 tsp) gelatine
30 ml (2 Tbsp) water
250 ml (1 cup) cream
180 ml (¾ cup) sifted icing sugar
5 ml (1 tsp) vanilla essence
1 x 250 g tub smooth, low-fat cottage cheese
10 ml (2 tsp) finely shredded fresh mint leaves

Rinse and hull the berries, pat absolutely dry, then chop into small pieces. For a velvety soft-serve, whizz all the berries in a blender until smooth; for a slightly chunkier texture, reserve one-quarter of the chopped berries, and fold these in later, along with the mint. Sprinkle the gelatine onto the water in a small container, then dissolve over simmering water – do not overheat. Add to the purée and pulse briefly to mix. Whip the cream with the icing sugar and vanilla essence until stiff, then gently stir in the cottage cheese until it's all nice and smooth. Add the purée and the mint, then fold in the reserved chopped berries, if using this option. Keep folding over gently until combined but not uniformly pink – a slightly marbled effect is attractive. Pour, or spoon, into 6–8 glasses or goblets and place in the coldest part of the refrigerator to firm up – a few hours, or even overnight, loosely covered. Decoration is optional – although mint leaves have become boring and dated, a tiny sprig would actually be appropriate, otherwise a small strawberry, if you have any left, otherwise leave plain. **Serves 6–8.**

Fruity Cupcakes

These look like brown muffins, but they're not. Based on a carrot cake mixture,
they're dense with fruit and spices and, topped with butter icing*,
they make perfect, single-serving little cakes.

2 large free-range eggs
125 ml (½ cup) light brown sugar
125 ml (½ cup) oil
250 ml (1 cup) flour – cake,
plain white or brown
2 ml (½ tsp) bicarbonate of soda
5 ml (1 tsp) baking powder
a tiny pinch of sea salt
2 ml (½ tsp) ground cinnamon
1 ml (¼ tsp) ground mixed spice
125 ml (½ cup) fruit cake mix
60 ml (4 Tbsp) finely chopped,
pitted dates
2 medium or 1 jumbo carrot,
coarsely grated (125 g)
60 ml (4 Tbsp) chopped walnuts
2 ml (½ tsp) vanilla essence
white butter icing and walnut
halves for topping

* If preferred, you could forget the
icing, and simply top each with
a nut before baking.
Also good, and less sweet.

Whisk the eggs and sugar. Add the oil and whisk very well until the mixture becomes creamy and a pale butterscotch in colour. Sift the dry ingredients – you can sift them straight into the creamed mixture (if using brown flour, add any bran left in the sieve). Combine well, then stir in the fruit mix, dates, carrot, nuts and essence. Have the muffin tin ready and waiting – you'll need a large one, to take 10 paper cups (the big cups with a base diameter of 4 cm) – one cup in each hollow. Fill each cup to two-thirds full. Bake at 160 °C for 30–35 minutes until richly browned and well risen; test with a skewer, it should come out clean when they're done. (Note that these cakes do not peak, but have smooth, rounded tops.) Leave to cool in the pan before lifting out in their paper cases. Top each with a small blob of icing, smooth over with a damp spatula (don't be too concerned about wavy edges, they must look homespun) and lightly press in the halved nuts. **Makes 10.**

Light Choc-nut Orange Cake with Dark Fudgy Icing

An easy, beat-'n-bake cake that looks gorgeous blanketed with velvety chocolate icing.

450 ml (1⅘ cups) cake flour
60 ml (4 Tbsp) cocoa powder
15 ml (1 Tbsp) baking powder
a pinch of sea salt
300 ml (1⅕ cups) castor sugar
150 ml (⅗ cup) oil
finely grated rind of 1 large orange
3 XL free-range eggs (unbeaten and at room temperature)
5 ml (1 tsp) vanilla essence
60 ml (¼ cup) milk
60 ml (¼ cup) water
100 g walnuts, chopped, except for a few halves for decoration

Sift the dry ingredients into a large bowl. Make a well in the centre and add the oil, orange rind, eggs, vanilla, milk and water, one ingredient at a time, in the order listed. Using an electric whisk, whisk on high speed until smooth – maximum 1½ minutes. Quickly but gently fold in the walnuts, and turn the mixture into a 22 cm cake tin, base and sides oiled and lined with baking paper. Spread evenly and tap once on the table top, before baking on the middle shelf of the oven at 180 °C. (If using a springform tin, place a baking tray on the lower rack in case of drips.) Bake for 50 minutes. Test with a skewer and, if done, stand for several minutes before turning out to cool. When cold, place the cake upside down on a large cake plate and brush the flat base (which is now the top) with a little melted smooth apricot jam and ice (see below).

Dark chocolate icing

In a heavy-based saucepan, over low heat, melt 150 g dark chocolate, broken up, with 15 ml (1 Tbsp) butter and 60 ml (¼ cup) water. When just smooth, switch off the stove plate and add presifted icing sugar, 50 ml (⅕ cup) at a time, stirring until it disappears before continuing. You will need about 250 ml (1 cup) in total. As soon as the mixture becomes thick but is still pourable, drizzle it evenly over the cold cake, allowing it to run down the sides – work quickly, as it firms up rapidly and you want to achieve a smooth, glossy finish. Gently press in a few walnuts here and there, and leave for several hours to set. **Makes 10 large wedges.**

FLOP-PROOF SCONES

Scones need to be enjoyed when freshly baked, and these are last-minute life-savers –
especially if you're running a Coffee Shop – because all it takes is a quick sift, whisk, pat
and bake (no butter to rub in, no aerating, no fuss) to produce a billow of fat scones
to pile with jam and thick cream. With this in mind, oil is used instead of butter.
The wholesome, fruity version is another easy option.

Plain golden scones

500 ml (2 cups) cake flour
20 ml (4 tsp) baking powder
1 ml (¼ tsp) sea salt
30 ml (2 Tbsp) castor sugar
1 large free-range egg
60 ml (¼ cup) each oil,
milk and water
5 ml (1 tsp) fresh lemon juice
beaten egg or milk to glaze

Sift the dry ingredients into a mixing bowl. Whisk together the remaining ingredients. Add to the sifted mixture and mix lightly, using a firm spatula and then, using your hands, quickly shape into a soft ball – flouring your hands if necessary. Pat out into a 2 cm thick circle or rectangle on a lightly floured board; don't be heavy-handed, but the dough needs to be given a quick knead and smoothing out to remove any surface cracks. Cut out, using either a 6 cm round cutter, flouring it after every second scone, or cut into squares with a floured knife. Gather up any off-cuts and pat out smoothly again to give you 8 scones in total. Place fairly close together, but not quite touching, on a baking sheet lined with baking paper. Brush tops with egg or milk, and bake near the top of the oven at 220 °C for 15 minutes until well-risen and golden. Remove to a rack to cool down before serving. Scones should be carefully broken in half, not cut, before spreading. **Makes 8.**

Chunky brown scones

250 ml (1 cup) white bread flour
20 ml (4 tsp) baking powder
1 ml (¼ tsp) salt
15 ml (1 Tbsp) castor sugar
5 ml (1 tsp) ground cinnamon
250 ml (1 cup) wholewheat flour
125 ml (½ cup) fruit cake mix
30 ml (2 Tbsp) sunflower seeds
1 large free-range egg
60 ml (¼ cup) each oil,
milk and water
5 ml (1 tsp) fresh lemon juice
beaten egg or milk to glaze

Sift the white flour, baking powder, salt, castor sugar and cinnamon, then mix in the wholewheat flour, fruit and seeds. Whisk the remaining ingredients together and add to the flour mixture, then complete as in the previous recipe, but extend the baking time to 18 minutes. **Makes 8.**

Buttermilk Muffins with Cheese and Sun-dried Tomatoes

Bake, break and serve warm with butter and an eggy dish, or with soup,
or for elevenses with coffee instead of something sweet.

500 ml (2 cups) bran-rich self-raising flour (or use white self-raising, or half and half)

2 ml (½ tsp) mustard powder

2 ml (½ tsp) salt

10 ml (2 tsp) castor sugar

2 pickling onions, coarsely grated

2 ml (½ tsp) dried mixed herbs

90 ml (6 Tbsp) finely snipped sun-dried tomatoes (first drained on kitchen paper if in oil)

60 g cheddar cheese, grated

60 ml (4 Tbsp) finely chopped parsley

1 XL free-range egg

250 ml (1 cup) buttermilk

60 ml (¼ cup) oil

about 50 g extra cheddar cheese, and paprika for topping

Sift the flour, mustard powder, salt and castor sugar into a mixing bowl, adding any bran left in the sieve. Mix in the onions, dried herbs, tomatoes, cheese and parsley. Whisk together the egg, buttermilk and oil. Make a well in the dry ingredients and pour in the liquid. Stir quickly and lightly until the ingredients are just combined – do not try to smooth the batter, it should be lumpy. Spoon into 10 large, lightly oiled hollows in a muffin pan (not paper cups), dividing equally. Top generously with extra grated cheese, dust with paprika and bake immediately at 200 °C for 25 minutes, until risen and golden brown. Place on a rack to cool down briefly before gently removing the muffins. **Makes 10.**

Nutty Brown Banana Muffins with Honey Butter

Served freshly baked, broken in half and spread with a dab of the special butter,
these moreish muffins are at their delicious best – but then
they're also good enough to enjoy just as they are.

500 ml (2 cups) cake flour
a pinch of sea salt
5 ml (1 tsp) baking powder
5 ml (1 tsp) bicarbonate of soda
5 ml (1 tsp) ground mixed spice
125 ml (½ cup) castor sugar
50 g walnuts, chopped
3 jumbo or 4 medium ripe bananas
80 ml (⅓ cup) melted butter
(60 g before melting)
125 ml (½ cup) milk
1 XL free-range egg
5 ml (1 tsp) vanilla essence

Sift the flour, salt, baking powder, bicarb and spice into a large bowl. Mix in the sugar and the walnuts. In a separate bowl, mash the bananas and mix in the melted butter. Whisk the remaining ingredients together and then whisk into the bananas. Pour the mixture into the dry ingredients and mix quickly to a loose batter; do not smooth it out – just fold over until no trace of flour remains. Pour, or spoon, into 12 large, lightly oiled muffin pan cups – they should be two-thirds full. Bake at 180 °C for 25 minutes, or until firm and richly browned. Leave to stand for a few minutes before easing out, and placing on a rack to cool. If desired, serve with the honey butter (see below). **Makes 12 large muffins.**

Honey butter

If using, whip 60 g soft butter until creamy, then add 30–45 ml (2–3 Tbsp) honey (fynbos or veldflower are both good) and whisk until combined.

Gooseberry Muffins

Basic, soft muffins made special with the addition of golden Cape gooseberries.
These are available in cans, which means you don't have to have a bush
and can make them all year round. Affirm the gooseberry flavour by serving
these muffins with a pot of gooseberry jam, and a fluff of whipped cream.

500 ml (2 cups) cake flour
15 ml (1 Tbsp) baking powder
1 ml (¼ tsp) sea salt
60 ml (4 Tbsp) castor sugar
1 x 410 g can golden Cape
gooseberries, very well drained
and gently patted dry
60 ml (¼ cup) oil
1 large free-range egg
125 ml (½ cup) milk
125 ml (½ cup) water
5 ml (1 tsp) vanilla essence
ground cinnamon for topping

Sift together the flour, baking powder, salt and castor sugar. Gently mix in the berries, just until coated with flour – be careful not to mash them. Whisk together the oil, egg, milk, water and vanilla essence, and pour into a well in the centre of the dry ingredients. Mix together lightly, then spoon into 10 oiled muffin cups (not paper cases), filling them two-thirds full. Sprinkle with cinnamon and bake at 200 °C for 20–22 minutes until risen and a pale, golden brown. Some of the gooseberries might pop out of the tops. Just pop them back, and leave to stand a few minutes before removing to a rack to cool. **Makes 10 fairly large muffins.**

SMOOTHIES

Anyone with a blender and a few pieces of fruit can make a smoothie.
Smoothies can be anything from a healthy, pure-fruit slurp, to a lush
sort of milkshake, to a whole breakfast in a glass. The following are simple variations
on the basic theme; **salubrious and low fat**, they are too thick to drink, and should be
eaten slowly, with a small spoon.

Winter smoothie

Place in a blender: 200 g really ripe and sweet papaw or papino, peeled and diced (peeled weight); 60 ml (¼ cup) fresh orange juice; ½ large banana, sliced; ½ sweet apple, peeled and chopped; 30 ml (2 Tbsp) vanilla yoghurt. Whizz until smoothly thick. If too chunky for your blender, add extra orange juice or yoghurt. You could also use plain yoghurt and a drizzle of honey – the sweet secret of smoothies is that they're so easy to adapt to personal taste. **Makes about 300 ml (1⅕ cups).**

Spring smoothie

Place in a blender: 4 large, ripe strawberries (about 70 g), rinsed, hulled and chopped and sprinkled with 10 ml (2 tsp) castor sugar. Leave to stand for a few minutes until sugar has dissolved, then add: 1 large banana, sliced; 30 ml (2 Tbsp) plain, fat-free yoghurt; 10–15 ml (2–3 tsp) fat-reduced cream. Whizz until smooth. **Makes about 250 ml (1 cup).**

Summer smoothie

1 large, blush-coloured dessert peach (e.g. Evans)	Peel and slice the peach and mango and tip into a blender, adding all the juices from the chopping
1 large mango	board. Whizz to blend – as these fruits are soft,
15 ml (1 Tbsp) fat-free milk powder	they should purée easily. Add the milk powder
30 ml (2 Tbsp) water	and water, blend well, then sweeten if necessary.
honey or sugar if necessary	**Makes about 325 ml (1⅓ cups).**

GLOSSARY

ag Oh. Used to express exasperation

bakkie A light truck with an open back, often used for carrying goods or people

berg Mountain

blerrie Bloody

bredies Stews

buchu A medicinal plant, sometimes infused in brandy, mainly used for stomach complaints

dominee A minister or clergyman

donga A ditch or gully caused by soil erosion

ja Yes

kloof A deep ravine or valley

knip To wink

kopjes Small hills

lekker A colloquial term meaning anything from pleasant to delicious

liefie Term of affection, Afrikaans for 'lovey'

oblietjies Crisp, rolled wafers

perlemoen Abalone

riempie Softened hide used for thonging seats and backs of chairs

sjoe Phew!

soetpatats A dish of sweet potatoes

sporran The pouch that hangs from a belt in front of a kilt.

stoep Veranda

tannie Auntie

tripple A type of gait, usually used when referring to a type of Boer pony

veld The South African countryside

voetsek Be off!

voorkamer The front room of a house

vrek To die

CONVERSION TABLE		
METRIC	US CUPS	IMPERIAL
5 ml	1 tsp	3⁄16 fl oz
15 ml	1 Tbsp	½ fl oz
60 ml	4 Tbsp (¼ cup)	2 fl oz
80 ml	⅓ cup	2¾ fl oz
125 ml	½ cup	4½ fl oz
160 ml	⅔ cup	5½ fl oz
200 ml	¾ cup	7 fl oz
250 ml	1 cup	9 fl oz
100 g	–	3½ oz
250 g	–	9 oz
500 g	–	1 lb
750 g	–	1¾ lb
1 kg	–	2¼ lb

OVEN TEMPERATURES		
CELSIUS	FAHRENHEIT	GAS MARK
100 °C	200 °F	¼
110 °C	225 °F	¼
120 °C	250 °F	½
140 °C	275 °F	1
150 °C	300 °F	2
160 °C	325 °F	3
180 °C	350 °F	4
190 °C	375 °F	5
200 °C	400 °F	6
220 °C	425 °F	7
230 °C	450 °F	8
240 °C	475 °F	9

RECIPE INDEX